Refined in the Furnace of Affliction: Nearly 30 years with Chronic Fatigue Syndrome/M.E.

R. Paul Gregory.
Educational Psychologist.

Published by Hallmark Press International Ltd.
County Durham, U.K.

Published by Hallmark Press International Ltd.
34, Lambton Court, Peterlee, County Durham, SR8 1NG. U.K.
Tel: (0191)5873886 International: +44 (0) 1915873886.
Email: hallmarkpress@btinternet.com
Website: www.hallmarkpress.co.uk

ISBN 978-1-906459-19-2

Date April 2008.

Printed and bound by CPI Antony Rowe, Eastbourne

To my wife and daughters.

About the author.

Paul Gregory graduated with a B.Sc.(Hons.) in Psychology from Durham University in 1968 and a Post Graduate Certificate of Education (PGCE) in 1969. After three years teaching followed by an M.Ed. (Educational Psychology), at Birmingham University he worked as a chartered educational psychologist for Birmingham Education Authority. During this time he published over 40 articles and a book 'Action Research in the Secondary School' with Routledge. In 1988 he had to take early retirement from his career because of C.F.S./M.E. until Easter 1991 when he started a private practice for dyslexia, educational and psychological assessments. Careful daily management of activity enables him to work part-time, but he is still seriously affected by this condition.

Contents.

PART 3. A SCIENTIFIC PERSPECTIVE ON C.F.S./M.E.

List of Figures.

List of Tables.

Acknowledgements.

I would like to acknowledge my gratitude for the continued assistance from the staff at the Sutton Coldfield Reference Library in sending for books and copies of journal articles from the British Library, Boston Spa. This book would not have been possible without their help.

Thanks should also go the Barnes Medical Library at Birmingham University who conducted a computer search of the medical literature on C.F.S./M.E. for me.

Also thanks should go to Dr. Charles Shepherd medical director of the M.E. Association and Stephanie Woodcock of the editorial panel, through their service to readers of the Association's Perspectives magazine.

Much is owed to my professional colleague Dr. Raj Gupta for his support through-out my illness.

I am very grateful to Yvette Thompson for her continued encouragement to believe in my work and persevere in finding a publisher.

And I would not have recovered without the love of my wife and daughters.

Preface.

I, the author, have suffered from C.F.S./M.E. since 1980, although the illness was not diagnosed as Chronic Fatigue Syndrome until 1988 when it was called M.E. (Myalgic Encephalomyelitis).

It is hoped that this book will be of benefit to people in a similar predicament and those professionals who work with them. Both need to understand the process of the illness and the knowledge required to promote recovery.

If I have learnt anything from being ill with C.F.S./M.E. it is that we are all travellers in space, on Earth, making a cosmic journey of a lifetime. To travel alone can be precarious. To make the best of the experience, we need the companionship of each other and the wisdom of those who have gone before.

Most mental turmoil comes to us as a result of our attempts, to cope with life's stresses, to avoid emotional pain and to seek immediate rather than long term happiness.

This book is an account of some of the experiences that I have gleaned in exploring the phenomenon of C.F.S./M.E. It was not written all at once but like Kafka's story of the Great Wall of China, in very small manageable sections.

Inspiration for this account came from reading about Renate Dorrestein's experience in her book entitled "Heden Ik" (The one I am now.") published in Amsterdam in 1993. It tells the story of Renate's illness with M.E. and is full of wisdom and humour.

Considering all of the valuable medical research undertaken into C.F.S./M.E. around the world, there is surprisingly little that is directly useable or useful to relieve the on-going day to day suffering of patients. The people who have written books about this topic have largely been medical doctors.

I have the belief that the right knowledge gives the reader who is affected by this illness the power to set about improving his or her life, by making informed choices.

In the book the medical vocabulary has been explained as far as possible, in order to improve the readers' comprehension of such literature in the future.

For me the experience of C.F.S./M.E. has been the single most horrific period of my life. I nearly did not make it. It has not been just a physical illness but much more than that. It has been chronic; disabling. It has brutally changed my whole existence. From being a confident successful full-time educational psychologist, researcher and writer, I became chronically ill and unemployable.

However, the most important task I have ever achieved, has been coping with this disease and for the time-being, finding a partial solution. I have returned to a pleasant and enjoyable life, by using many of the ideas and information described in this book. Many other people have done the same, **but some have not**. Success depends on treatment, a personal strategy guided by knowledge and the support of family and friends.

But I am under no illusions. One bad mistake, miscalculation or unforeseen event causing over-exertion and I could relapse and be set back years. I am not cured.

After struggling to carry on working for eight years with C.F.S./M.E., ill-health forced me to take early retirement at the age of 41. Two and a half years of severe illness followed, after which I began a long slow recovery. I am now working part-time as a psychologist in a private capacity and writing. My wife used to be a part-time secondary school teacher before she retired.

This book is a description of my journey to better times and I hope that it will help others to find their way out of C.F.S./M.E.

April 2008.   R. Paul Gregory.

Introduction.

After years of controversy about whether or not C.F.S./M.E. even exists, an expert government report has recognised that C.F.S./M.E. once known as "Yuppie Flu" is a real physical illness and should not be regarded as something that was "all in the mind" (The Report of the C.F.S./M.E. Working Group to the Chief Medical Officer (2002); a copy of which can be downloaded from the website: www.doh.gov.uk by typing 'cfs' into the search box and scanning down the list of publications).

The chief medical officer, Professor Sir Liam Donaldson, has published guidance on the management of the condition that has been made available to doctors and other health care professionals. The report also states that C.F.S./M.E. should be classed as a chronic condition with long-term effects on health, alongside other illnesses such as motor neurone disease and multiple sclerosis.

The National Institute for Health and Clinical Excellence (N.I.C.E, see website www.nice.org.uk) has also issued guidelines for the management of C.F.S./M.E. These can be obtained by visiting the website and typing 'C.F.S./M.E.' into the search box on the homepage.

Some years ago there were estimated to be between 100 and 200,000 people in the U.K. and about 1.4 million in the English speaking world suffering from C.F.S./M.E. assuming the same prevalence rate. Recently this estimate has increased by about 250 per cent.

There are a number of names used to describe this illness, including Post Viral Fatigue Syndrome (P.V.F.S.) for the first six months of the illness. However the main characteristics are, relapsing fatigue preceded by an onset involving a viral infection; flu, cold or sore-throat. M.E. stands for myalgic encephalomyelitis meaning that it is an inflammation of the central nervous system and muscles. It is listed as a disease of the nervous system by the World Health Organisation.

Many researchers around the world have used the name "Chronic Fatigue Syndrome" (C.F.S.) as synonymous with "Myalgic Encephalomyelitis" (M.E.).

I became ill in 1980 and had to retire as a consequence from my career in 1988.

For a long time I have asked myself how I have managed to become chronically ill with C.F.S./M.E. What did I do wrong? Why was I never warned? Was it just bad luck and down to chance? By the end of this book I hope I will be a little closer to knowing and be able to provide some suggestions to help the next generation avoid it.

In January 1991, after a long period of gradual improvement, I felt well enough not only to review the medical research in an attempt to understand my illness more fully, but also to search for strategies that might alleviate some of the symptoms of C.F.S./M.E. that can greatly restrict your life and happiness.

I think that there is a great deal of medical evidence to show that C.F.S./M.E. is a physical illness, but there are huge potential psychological problems likely to occur because of a) the chronic nature of C.F.S./M.E. b) the associated depression and c) its impact on the life of the sufferer and their family.

I do recognise that most of the medical research so far has resulted in more understanding, but provided only treatments of limited effect. Whilst you wait for an eventual cure, you have to cope as best you can with the disease, on a day to day basis. This can be very hard. It has been known to blight the lives of many sufferers, result in suicide and lead to the break-up of some families.

Knowledge of C.F.S./M.E. in general, could mean the difference between coping with the illness and having a fulfilled life, or being permanently wretched, miserable or suicidal.

This book is divided into three parts. **Part 1** descries in detail, my experience of living with C.F.S./M.E. and that of my wife and family in their caring role. It provides a real picture of what this illness means.

Sometimes after re-reading this first part, I worry that it is over-stated. But then I remember - and realise that it is not. Definitely not. Reality is a difficult picture to paint with words and you inevitably fall short.

The spiritual and philosophical insights that I have learned from the years of ordeal with the illness are related in the **second part**. Many quotations are from the Bible, which is not only a religious work but, I have realized, a record of the wisdom, generations of people have learnt from living their lives.

Part 3 provides a scientific perspective and discusses the current medical findings for C.F.S./M.E. summarizing the main points about the causes and treatments.

PART 1. A PERSONAL CASE HISTORY.

CHAPTER 1. IN THE BEGINNING.

A COMMON EXPERIENCE?

I think there is more to falling ill with C.F.S./M.E. than implied by explanatory theories of viral infections and the body's immune system. In one week recently I had three telephone calls from sufferers living in different parts of the U.K. Their stories were surprisingly similar to my own. Their names have been changed to protect their identity.

The first was Malcolm aged 58. He used to be a high-powered area manager for a multi-million pound retail company. He loved his work until he was forced to retire because of C.F.S./M.E. some years ago. When he contracted the illness he was working very hard and paid little attention to the initial infection. He never properly recovered. His attitude to illness has been transformed by his own. He reluctantly admitted with an air of embarrassed shame, that when carrying out his job he was very unsympathetic to employees complaining of illness or chronic health conditions. Talking to me, he was very penitent and sad because he was not in a position to make recompense to the working people he had misjudged.

Dave aged 48 was the next; a chartered engineer who worked very hard and did not realise the dangers in taking longer and longer to recover from hepatitis and glandular fever. A subsequent mild chest infection resulted in C.F.S./M.E. **Now he cannot work at all.**

Lastly there was Carol aged 44; a statistician of some merit and ability, working for a large pharmaceutical company. She loved her job and similarly worked very hard but now has been forced to retire because of C.F.S./M.E.

The commonality with my own case is the love we all had for our jobs and working very hard at the time of an infectious illness. The question is, have other people succumbed to this chronic illness **in the same way**? All I can do is to describe my story and ask other sufferers to compare it with their own.

In an effort to understand and gain control of my illness and render it more predictable I have kept a detailed diary of events since first becoming ill. Some doctors call this supposedly unhealthy interest in one's own illness, hypochondriasis. I call it an aid to survival.

AUGUST 1979.
It was August 1979 on the beach near Abersoch in North Wales, during a heat wave, holidaying with my wife and two daughters then aged six and three, where I start my story. Reading about the murder of Lord Mountbatten and his courageous exploits during World War 2, I began thinking about how I would have coped in such situations. I had no idea. I did not know my own limitations really. I was aged 32.

It was a beautiful day and with curiosity about my own capabilities I resolved to swim from one side of the bay to the other, to see if I could do it. I did. It took over an hour. I was very pleased.

This was the start of some subtle changes of attitude building through September as I returned to work. I had been employed as a psychologist for Birmingham Education Authority for six years. I enjoyed the job immensely. After teaching socially disadvantaged primary school children, my new job allowed me to put psychology to work for the benefit of such children in my casework with individuals.

I helped children with phobias return to school and those with problem behaviour become more manageable and therefore more acceptable, both at home and at school. In the previous term I had published my first research paper. Trying to emulate the behaviour and achievements of a couple of colleagues, I read psychology avidly and resolved to improve further the quality of my casework as well as do research. I started projects at three schools, in September 1979; one for children with language disorders, and two for those with reading difficulties in a primary and a secondary school. These were to be a big demand on my time and energy. My wife will tell you that an Achille's heel of mine is not being able to judge very well how long a task will take.

I am over-optimistic about how much I can do. And then reluctant to reduce my commitment to what has been started. At a time when I was not only unsure of my own limitations, but also fired with altruism to help the socially disadvantaged, write publishable papers and do research, I was influenced by the writing of Alexander Solzhenitsyn. His book, 'Cancer Ward', about young people dying of cancer had a great effect on me. As I worked and lived, I speculated about what it would be like to be told you only had three months to live. What would I do? I would, I decided, try to fit a lifetime's ambitions into three months. Imperceptibly unconsciously such fantasies drove me to work harder.

Occasionally I went to church with my family but idly dismissed much of it as not really relevant to me. However it does provide a Christian philosophy of life. Though I was unaware of it at this time, I was formulating a new philosophy as can be seen from the above.

Some people's ground plan for life involves a quest for money, happiness, pleasure, fame etc. but mine seemed more complex than these. It is only with age does one realise which philosophies have happy outcomes and which do not. I remember, ironically, that in October 1979, one evening, I thought to myself, I am really feeling good about my family, work, research and publications. I did not realise that it was based on a pace of life that was unsustainable.

Next I was commissioned to write a chapter for a colleague's book. Then I took up French classes at evening school as well as teaching my elder daughter to read and play chess. As the months passed it was getting more difficult to maintain all of these activities; added to which I was increasingly becoming angry with myself for not meeting my self-imposed daily targets of work. So I punished myself with verbal reprimands. I felt tired but took no notice. I could work over it. I had learned to ignore fatigue in training at secondary school where I enjoyed athletics, cross-country running and rugby. I also came to believe that I had only done a good days work, if I was really tired at the end of the day.

Interestingly my parents later told me, that as a toddler I would be active till I dropped exhausted, which contrasted with my two brothers who regulated activity with rest.

Ignoring fatigue, first learnt with sport, later transferred to academic and office work. With hindsight it was a destructive habit to acquire. It would have been better to learn how to pace myself; how to rest and conserve energy; how not to waste personal resources.

All of this work regime was self-inflicted. In retrospect I think I was addicted to the pleasure and the success I perceived in my work with disadvantaged children and in publishing the results. I was becoming a workaholic with A type behaviour. This describes a person who is governed by time, always working, rushing to achieve goals and never resting or relaxing. It is behaviour associated with heart disease. The wise would have seen what was coming, but I had no idea.

NOVEMBER 1979.

Catching a cold in November 1979 added to the burden, but fortified with the impression that I did not have time to be ill I pressed on. The cold turned into influenza and I was forced to take to my bed, but even there I carried on working.

One Sunday morning still ill, I sat on the edge of my bed in my pyjamas beginning to feel breathless. As I tried harder to breathe, taking bigger and bigger breaths, I shouted for my wife. I was beginning to panic as the deepest breaths I could manage did not have the desired effect. My wife asked if she should ring for the doctor; I nodded in agreement then said no there wasn't time but instead to call an ambulance. Desperation and the feeling that I must not pass out, concentrated the intensity of my breathing. The ambulance at last arrived. Gradually on the way to the hospital the tension eased. Sitting up on a hospital trolley a junior doctor explained that I had pneumonia and had been hyperventilating. Hadn't I realised he said. I had never heard of the condition, but I know now.

By the time my family and parents arrived I was sat up in bed feeling foolish, as if nothing had happened. I felt perfectly well. With the agreement of my G.P. I went back to work after 10 days in bed, resuming work as if all was well.

The next step on this treacherous journey to the abyss was developing an infected wisdom tooth. I spent the afternoon of Boxing Day (1979) in the out-patients department of Birmingham Dental Hospital with my father. Not a very good Christmas present. Painkillers and a second dose of antibiotics in a few months, gradually resolved the agony of what felt like tooth-ache, earache and a sore-throat all at the same time.

In January 1980 I was well enough to present a paper at a British Psychological Society conference; but I was beginning to feel an unusual fatigue. Working as usual, I carried on until tiredness took me to the doctor's again. Without apparent reference to my immediate medical history of infections, he prescribed Dartalan, a tranquillizer, enabling me to go back to work.

Eventually, after returning to the doctor fatigued again, he gave me three weeks off work. This was March 1980. He lead me to believe that each episode of illness was not related to any of the previous ones I had suffered since October. He treated each one separately.

With this respite drawing to a close, began a more sinister feeling. It was like a black millstone around my head casting a veil of darkness over all of my feelings and sensations. I felt very sad but had no words to describe it to my doctor. He consequently did not get the message.

Near desperation, with only my wife for support, I told the G.P. I could not stop thinking of suicide during every waking hour. I did not want to die or commit suicide but my imagination was out of control. My doctor understood this time. He asked me (a psychologist) if I wanted to see a psychiatrist or go into a psychiatric hospital. Whoever heard of a psychologist getting a psychiatric disorder. Yes, actually I do remember a professor of psychology describing his mental illness in the Sunday Observer some years ago.

By early afternoon a psychiatrist and his student called at my house. I was amazed to be on the other end of the interviewing process. I was usually meeting medics and discussing other people as cases.

"My God I'm a psychiatric case", dawned on me.

As if in answer to all my problems, the psychiatrist declared that I had endogenous depression as a result of influenza, then pneumonia, being run down and working too hard. After agreeing that the prescription of four 25 mg tablets of triptafen per day (an anti-depressant, amitriptyline and a tranquillizer, perphenazine in one tablet) prescribed by my G.P. was correct he left saying that my symptoms would gradually disappear over the next ten to 21 days.

I rated myself on a scale from one, for normal to five, terrible, four times a day as a measure of my depression. I started with waking then lunchtime, tea-time and evening. I soon noticed that I was worst on waking but gradually improved through-out the day, to being best, in fact normal, at about 10pm. I dreaded going to bed at night as it would herald the approach of another day and the start of the terrible cycle all over again.

I also kept a daily diary of my activities. This revealed that my depressive symptoms, obsessive thoughts and fantasies of suicide were occurring most, at times of high activity; for example if people came to stay for the weekend. Resting definitely assuaged all the symptoms but neither my G.P., psychiatrist nor myself had heard of C.F.S./M.E. at this stage. I was clearly diagnosed as having post-influenzal depression.

Every morning I would wake with a horrible black heavy shrouded feeling. There was no joy, there was no relief. I could bearly stand it. The pain in my head obliterated all other impressions. I feared never getting well; of losing my family and home; of becoming a vagrant.

In bed under the duvet, I felt I was the only person in a black universe. I decided there and then, that there must be a God. The otherwise dark emptiness was too hard to live with. I needed God.

Getting up and doing the routine tasks of living helped distract me for a few minutes from my agony. I oscillated between activities, trying not to be tired or bored, but rarely getting relief or comfort.

In the afternoon, my wife and I would go for a walk in Sutton Park and talk. The central issue was always how long it would take to recover, could I stand it. Suicidal fantasies were constant.

In the park we walked alongside a railway line. Instantly the thought of going under a train flashed through my mind. Then I saw the bridge; jumping off it would be another way. The fantasies popped into my head without my volition. They had a will of their own.

The only thing to sustain me was the knowledge that the anti-depressants should work eventually and that by 10pm in the evening I was always back to normal. Frequent physical contact in hugging my wife and daughters was very comforting.

APRIL 1980.
When the Easter holidays (April 1980) came, my wife and I wondered whether a short caravan holiday and change of scene would help. My G.P. thought it would. The family and I travelled to a caravan site near London. All the way down the route I kept imagining crashing the car into on-coming traffic. I didn't tell my family. I felt terrible. That first night brought a new twist to my illness.

I woke suddenly in a cold sweat, my heart racing. I felt extreme terror and anxiety. I wanted to get up and run; it was five o'clock in the morning. I imagined myself frantically running across the fields, half dressed, my wife reporting me to the police, people combing the countryside for me; a manhunt and then TV news-flashes. I cannot do it; they'd think I was mad, it would be Broadmoor. Don't hurt anyone or be violent whatever you do, I thought.

But why was this happening? I became more rational. What has changed? What is causing this? Then I realised. Could it be withdrawal symptoms due to dropping off the Dartalan too abruptly? I hurriedly took one and waited for a tense twenty minutes. I was feeling better. It worked. Later I realised I had just had my first panic attack. It is no wonder that some people become agoraphobic in their attempt to avoid them. Now I understood.

The holiday was a disaster. It should be a golden rule; never go on holiday to strange surroundings, foregoing the familiar and taking up new demands, when you are ill.

Curious dreams began to occur of meeting Christ in a huge cathedral. These recurred many times and eventually made me think that maybe God did not want me to commit suicide. I felt that He had come looking for me and not the reverse. But I still feared that I might be forced by the mental anguish to die in order to get relief.

At this time I made two promises. One was to my wife that I would not commit suicide however bad I felt and the second to God, that if I ever got out of this depression I'd get confirmed. The thought that God was on my side, has given me great strength at my lowest times. With God's support I felt that I could conquer anything. Gone were my disparaging views about church-goers. I was beginning to realise that the Christian ethic also provides a tried and tested way of life.

I studiously avoided listening to the TV news. People dying of starvation or in poverty increased my anguish and pain. I could only just cope with my own troubles, let alone anyone else's.

Gradually the drugs had their effect. I just had to be patient. My wife was tremendous. We talked a great deal, walked and comforted each other. At this time she was not working in her job. I remember too, television comedy had a very beneficial, if only short-lived, effect. Marti Caine had her own show on a Monday night at 8-15 pm. It was an island of pleasure in a sea of despair. Her beauty and humour were a tonic I looked forward to every week. These were the high points that made the goal of good health worth waiting for.

Well, it took a month to six weeks for the symptoms to completely clear and that was the longest month of my life.

By June respite was well on its way. I had discovered some ways of easing the depressive symptoms. I frequently lay down and cleared my mind to think of beautiful places and to tell myself I was getting better; that I was doing well; it would not be long; to just be patient. Keeping my diary, showed me that the bad days did pass and that there were times when I felt pleasure.

I listened to music and the radio. Also I had a list of very short tasks (or steps in a bigger task) that would take about 10 minutes to do. I alternated these with resting and frequently rewarded myself with nuts, chocolate and positive thoughts. This gave me a lovely feeling. I washed my hair every few days and kept myself clean and tidy. This helped. I was getting back some control.

Sunbathing on sunny but chilly days in my anorak gave me such a good tan on my face, my G.P. could not believe I was ill.

After 12 weeks off work I returned on June 9th 1980 to my job, very grateful and relieved. I thought the illness was over and had no notion of what was to come over the next 28 years. I lived in blissful ignorance of the pain that was awaiting me; so bad it would make this episode look like a picnic.

I reflected how unbelievable it was that flu should sometimes carry in its wake such a diabolical illness. The good news is that it is treatable taking only months to resolve instead of up to two years, as in the past, before anti-depressant drugs were available. (Later my research was to tell me that before effective medication many people with depression had only one recourse if they could stand it no longer. My heart goes out to them. I know their pain). I had made a mistake in my attitude to flu. I was certain not to do it again and taught my children the lesson for their good.

The only hint that I might be suffering from more than just post-influenzal depression, came in August 1980. At work I was enjoying using a calculator to work out the statistics to my research. Forgetting the time I inadvertently spent six hours that day doing this. By the end of the afternoon I was feeling very ill and decided not to do any more that week. I soon recovered but did not realise that my brain had been affected by my illness. My brother, agreed to calculate my statistics and in his typically unassuming way he wrote a computer program to calculate analysis of covariance that would then analyse my results.

AUGUST 1980.

Over the next two years I was not ill again. Life was fulfilling both at home and work. I still saw the psychiatrist every few months to tell him my progress in reducing the triptafen medication; my main pre-occupation being unable to drink alcohol when taking anti-depressants.

Every time I saw the psychiatrist I complained of fatigue following every reduction of dosage. He always maintained that this was uncharacteristic of depression. Because of this fatigue I had to manage myself very carefully. At work still full-time, I took regular breaks, stopped all sporting activity, avoided swimming as the cold water seemed to drain me of energy and I frequently rewarded myself for keeping to this careful management. I discovered that rewarding myself with positive thoughts (avoiding negative ones) nuts, chocolate, oranges, speciality tea in tea-shops, opera, going to church and relaxation were all good things. I particularly valued my family as never before. Without quite realising it, my philosophy of life had become better adjusted.

NOVEMBER 1983.

By November 1983 at the age of 37 I had succeeded in reducing the medication from 35 tablets per week (5 per day) to just 4 per week. However, I developed a problem with not being able to fall asleep at night. On the days when I did not take a tablet, it would be 5-30 a.m. before I was able to drop off.

My G.P. said that exercise was the best thing to do, so I went for a walk and did a stint of weight training in my bedroom every evening. It did not work. What did, was discovering that I could get a lower dose tablet of the triptafen and take some each day. This was no thanks to my G.P. who said there wasn't one available.

JUNE 1984.
It was June 1984 before the next problem occurred. A week or so after spending all day servicing my caravan, an exhausting job, I began to get symptoms.

The heavy, unrelieved fatigue came first, then pains in all of my muscles and headaches, then the worries of not coping, having to cancel appointments, general anxiety and then fleeting but very real disturbing suicidal and bizarre fantasies. Each time they ran through my mind I'd try to stop them but they were too elusive.

These fantasies were legion. Initially they were very disturbing especially when I did hear occasionally on TV news items of someone acting out one of my fantasies. However I came to believe I would never carry out any of them. I was relieved to think they were only symptoms of my depression and that anti-depressants and rest had banished them in the past.

These symptoms would come some time after any physical activity. I went sick. None of the doctors took any notice when I told them. They just said put the dose of triptafen up till I felt better.

This process dribbled on till at last I was normal again, back on five triptafen per day. After four months off, I started work again in October 1984. I did not realise until years later that the extreme effort of servicing my caravan had probably caused this relapse; a C.F.S./M.E. relapse.

A year later, referral to a hospital physician revealed that the triptafen was causing my heart to beat rapidly, making me feel tired. I was prescribed Timolol, a beta blocker drug, and my fatigue improved.

MAY 1986.

By May 1986 after two years of reducing my drugs I was again on a very low dose. I was very pleased with my progress. It was time for me to service my caravan again. This done I very gradually began to get all of my symptoms back again. I was dismayed. I could not understand what was happening to me and nor could my G.P. or psychiatrist.

I had to stop work. Often sex was the only pleasurable event, when all rewards seemed to lose their effect. Even though at times I felt desperately exhausted, physical contact with my family never lost its capacity to comfort.

What I discovered later were called 'extrasystoles' made sleeping a nightmare. I would be just dropping off to sleep and then burst awake totally bewildered. It was caused by exaggerated heart beats. I would lie awake for hours not daring to go to sleep as I feared dying. In the end I was so fed up with worrying, I got to the stage where I couldn't care less about what might happen. I just went to sleep. In fact these extrasystoles can be caused by heart disease, smoking or caffeine but are quite common in normal individuals. There are drugs that can suppress them.

It was at this time, worried by the possibility of never working again I took out a permanent health insurance policy that would provide an income in such an event. The company, however, included an exclusion clause to say that the policy would not operate if I was ill with any psychiatric illness. At home I constantly went through the cycle of being too tired to do anything, resting, getting bored, fearing activity, doing a task eventually, and then worrying I'd done too much.

I feared being confined to bed for months or indefinitely. I did not understand my illness. It was unpredictable. What was the right course of action? I felt just like the anxiety-ridden mole in Kafka's story "The Burrow" in which it built a fantastic system of escape routes from his home underground. But it became so worried about being trapped underground that it decided to hide in the grass on the surface so that it could see from where its would-be-attacker came. This in fact made the mole even more vulnerable than ever, as it was now outside!

Too tired and depressed to do anything I ruminated about how surprising it was, in such a state of mind, to become sensitive to the problems of other people. The disasters and tragedies reported every day on TV now took on huge proportions. I mentally imagined in detail, the last anguished hours of the victims and then the trauma suffered by the relatives. All was in great emotional reality making such tragedies very hard to cope with. The only way to bear it was to avoid such reportage.

A merciful loving God must suffer such anguish at each and every human debacle occurring in the world. When one knows that 30,000 children alone, die of starvation across the globe everyday, the sum total of human suffering, daily, weekly, annually becomes unimaginable. It truely must be a great God who copes with this knowledge. Maybe this state I was in, was a glimpse into God's burden. Maybe not everyone ever experiences this and maybe it's a privilege; but it cannot be borne for long.

When I had completely recovered, I coped with impunity the daily catalogue of calamity and adversity reported in the media. Such a state of mind is described as normality, but surely does not the insight, available only to the depressed, not have more veracity?

Does not such experience give an incredible insight into human psychology.

This time though, I put my triptafen back up to five per day immediately and in six weeks I was back at work; pleased to be returning but demoralised that I had lost all of the good endeavour in coming off these tablets.

Every time I had a relapse of this inexplicable illness I learnt yet more about myself, though frankly I could have done without the lessons. My wife had been the main reason for my recovery each time. I have discovered she has qualities of love, care and compassion that I had never dreamt she had.

And I began to realise how peace of mind is a prerequisite to all happiness.

You can inadvertently slide into unhappiness by the way you think and the state of your self-esteem can be central to this thinking about yourself. I am sure my self-esteem, which has undulated through-out my life, was involved in my succumbing to C.F.S./M.E.

Passing the eleven plus gave it a boost, but being placed in form 1D in the first year gave it a knock. Gaining good G.C.E. O'levels was a credit but disappointing A'levels was depressing. At each low point I have struggled to restore my self-esteem. At university, passing, at the end of the first year on to the chemistry and psychology courses was an accomplishment but later I was disappointed with my degree. Gaining a masters degree in training as an educational psychologist and my first published papers were very pleasing but getting tired and over-working through striving to achieve my own self-imposed goals, I developed an anger at not being able to produce more. This reduced my self-esteem which craved more achievement to maintain itself. This could have been done easily by quietly reflecting on my past successes, but I did not think to do that. This illustrates how you automatically monitor your own behaviour and make a judgement about it, thus causing constant modification of your motivation and activities in order to maintain self-esteem at a high level. Self-esteem is based on the extent to which your goals (derived from your philosophy of life) are being achieved. If there is a large gap between achievement and aspirations, the self-esteem is low, where as if this gap is small, self-esteem is high.

Over-work and fatigue, had, I think led me into this vicious circle. Cognisant of the sin of pecuniary greed, I was unfamiliar with what in retrospect I have come to realise was an avaricious need for publications and an intoxication and addiction to the power to help others in my work.

I have often wondered why at the **height** of my professional development, I should start having a **lowered** self-esteem. A parallel, is described by Cooper (1981) for academic professors in universities. He found that low self-esteem, a symptom of stress, is related to qualitative work overload. The greater the "quality" of work expected for the professors, the lower the self-esteem. It meant that they were constantly having to perform intellectually demanding and unfamiliar work. Constantly performing such difficult work lowers confidence and self-esteem because one is not practised and expert at it.

However things were about to change. Recovered, I went to an appointment with my psychiatrist. First the good news. He said he had been reading the Sunday Observer over the weekend and he now knew what I was suffering from.

It was **MYALGIC ENCEPHALOMYELITIS - M.E.!** It was July 1986.

Now for the bad news. He judged it was for me, all psychological in origin. He said I was in danger of becoming a "professional invalid". I wondered whether this comment was meant to be psychotherapy; was it part of the treatment?

I was dismayed; but he replied that it was the best possibility. I would be able to resolve it. As it was not depression and therefore not a psychiatric disorder he said good bye to me and closed my case.

To date my symptoms had been fatigue following mild exercise, depression, anxiety, panic attacks, obsessional thoughts including suicide, hypoglycaemia, headaches, dry chest caused by talking, muscle tingling after exertion, fasciculation (spontaneous contractions of muscles most often occurring when in bed waiting to go to sleep) problems sleeping with extra systolic heartbeats and nightmares.

OCTOBER 1986.
With this judgement and the arrival of my fortieth birthday I heralded a new resolve. If it was all psychological in origin, then I should be able to beat it with enough will-power. Someone once said to me "where's your moral fibre?" I believed my psychiatrist's opinion and it prompted me to believe I could therefore overcome C.F.S./M.E. with sheer determination by disregarding all the pain; something I had learnt to do and was good at.

I was fed up with cossetting myself, being careful, no sport, no gardening or swimming that I had missed so much. I decided not to bother trying to reduce the dosage of four triptafen a day but instead, with this new decade I would strike out anew. I now knew I had M.E. but the devastating connection between exercise, physical and mental and the awful symptoms were never explained to me. It was to be left to me to discover and rediscover over and over again through the coming years. Throughout this term I tried to live and work normally with this new philosophy of life, but every few weeks I was having to take time off work because of very painful fatigue, suicidal fantasies, loss of appetite and anxiety. Maintaining my triptafen medication and rest resolved these symptoms and I would return to work.

Each time I did this return to normal life I gradually had a resumption of all these symptoms. This cycle carried on until eventually I was forced to take six weeks off work.

I tried to cope with the consequences of this new outlook but the harder I tried the worse I became. My psychiatrist's advice was to turn out to be terribly wrong, not just in a small measure but diametrically opposed to the right strategy. He nearly killed me.

During this period I ruminated about my life. I decided to avoid having deadlines for the completion of work. Because my wife had been at home full-time I'd allowed her to take over many household jobs. This had allowed my work to take up too large a part of my life. I resolved to put this right.

However, I had a constant fear of getting depression and the suicidal fantasies. I felt I had not achieved much in my life. Nostalgia about good days, when I was at college became very painful in reminiscence. But telling myself positive things about myself I discovered helped a great deal. A colleague from work who regularly telephoned lifted my spirits. Constantly there was a problem balancing rest with the need to do something to avoid boredom.

My illness was beginning to affect my relationship with my wife. She was continually worrying because her future was in my hands and dependent on the course of my illness. Feeling the strain she thought she was being neglected. The future was unpredictable. I feared her dying and worried about how I'd cope without her. This then upset her. I did not feel well enough to cope with any conflict so I largely left many of the decisions to her. I became dependent and deferential. I needed her support. This she gave continuously as well as working part-time teaching at this time. When alone in the house and feeling very low, just holding her jumpers and breathing in her fragrance, was sublime.

<u>MARCH 1987.</u>
I was due to return to work on Monday 16th March 1987. It may have been the apprehension that triggered the worst experience so far. It was 2-00 am. Friday morning. I woke terrified, and with a feeling of utter despair. The thought of suicide was uppermost.

My wife woke and was wonderful. We talked and eventually I decided to take an extra triptafen tablet. Half an hour later things calmed down. However, all the symptoms returned the next morning with a relentless intensity I'd never known before. There were constant thoughts and fantasies of suicide. I could find no way of controlling them. We rang my G.P. and he refused to come and see me. We were devastated. I rang my parents who were really supportive. My doctor did arrive in the afternoon and felt there was no need to go to a psychiatric hospital. He advised me to put up the triptafen to six per day. I did as he suggested but realised there would be a delay in their effect.

The weekend dragged on, with these symptoms unvarying in intensity, leaving me very near despair all the time. My wife was with me constantly. A second doctor came. Friends and relatives phoned. Every kindly gesture had a warming effect but this was short-lived. I remember vividly, my younger daughter coming to give me a love. There was still no relief. I was now seriously thinking of suicide as the only way of terminating the mental pain. It was a desolate feeling realising that I was probably beyond medical comprehension. The doctors did not really understand my illness and how to treat me.

The longest weekend I have ever experienced was punctuated by the arrival of the third doctor on the Monday afternoon. He was a psychiatrist from a psychiatric hospital. Very cold and austere, he forced me to give an account of my medical history, even though I was very tired and my wife had offered to relate it. He recommended going into hospital. Asking what it would be like, he replied curtly - "busy".
"Are you being facetious?" at my expense I replied.

"No but you are" he said acidly. He rated as the nastiest doctor I have ever encountered.

CHAPTER 2. THE DEBACLE.

PSYCHIATRIC HOSPITAL.

With much apprehension I was admitted to Ward M at 4p.m. that day and by the evening was being examined by a fourth doctor, a young woman. It was very thorough. Looking down my boxer shorts she said that she was just making sure I went out with the same number as I came in with. Wit seems to be a forte of psychiatrists. Or is it just **their** coping strategy?

I am pleased to say that my symptoms had completely resolved by the time of this encounter. It was probably due to the increased dose of triptafen eventually having an effect. I was hugely relieved.

A stay of nearly three weeks on Ward M proved to be a disturbing experience. The building was modern with individual bedrooms for some patients (myself included) with the rest being in two large dormitories. A spacious lounge/TV room revealed that most patients sat around in armchairs smoking cigarettes heavily. There were about fifty patients ranging in age from about 18 to 80. I discovered that many were suffering from depression but was grateful that all my symptoms except for fatigue had miraculously cleared. Coping with this environment I felt would be impossible if you were really ill.

Nearly all of the patients were sat in silence, some watching the TV; all looked dejected. Three black nurses sat talking animatedly to each other. I was to notice this a great deal. I constantly reflected on why all of this should happen to me. Tired, a nurse showed me to my room.

One of the first people I talked to in the dayroom, as the lounge was called, was a dark-haired man in his twenties to thirties in an old greasy navy suit. He was sat quietly rolling his own cigarette, balancing his tobacco tin on his lap whilst delicately licking the paper's edge and sticking it down to make his roll-up.

His name was Bob. He had been there three months. After several nervous breakdowns when he was at school he eventually got his own flat. Having many arguments with his family, they took out a court order restraining him from visiting their home. Breaking this resulted in a prison sentence. With an air of experience he judged this present ward to be like a hotel compared to being inside. His current crisis was caused when he discovered his flat had been burgled and all of his furniture missing. He went on the rampage with a machete, was picked up by the police and brought to this hospital. He felt pleased that he was going to a Salvation Army Hostel and the possibility of paid industrial therapy but had given up the idea of having his own flat again. I slowly realised that a burglary had tipped this fellow into mental illness and homelessness.

Suddenly as the hatch of the adjoining dining-room opened these sedentary figures, burst into life to form a queue. It was lunch-time.

That evening at about 10 pm in darkness I left my bed to go to the bathroom. Sleeping was difficult in this place, so a jaunt to the toilet broke the boredom. On my way back into my room I was shocked to see a faint figure in my bed. I was transfixed. I recognised that it was my room and nervously went in.

"Out of my bed you bastard" I said, coarsely in retrospect, as I realised that it was Checkers one of the other patients. Hurriedly the figure scrambled out and rapidly came towards me. I froze for a moment but he passed by me. He explained that he had made a genuine mistake. His room was next door I discovered. He was so apologetic that I felt guilty about my unseemly outburst. I reflected that I could have been more understanding but I didn't know what might happen in there. I over-reacted through fear.

A few days later and feeling a little more acclimatised I sat next to Olive. An old lady of 70 plus, she quietly told me she started with depression about a year after her husband had died. She was racked with worry. She was dreading having to go into an old people's home if she could not cope at home. She had problems with her feet and was anxious about not being able to walk from her home to the shops and back.

She had lost her confidence to live alone. Olive was to become a particular friend of mine. I discovered that age is no barrier to friendship. On every meeting she always asked about how I felt; something I discovered few others, including the staff, ever did.

Within days of my arrival I was frequently summoned to interviews with the junior doctor under the consultant psychiatrist. I told him how a little activity made me feel very tired and anxious.

Eventually I agreed to change from amitriptyline, the anti-depressant in the triptafen medication; triptafen consists of two drugs an anti-depressant and a tranquillizer. I was prescribed Clomipromine, another anti-depressant that is better for controlling obsessional thoughts like my suicidal fantasies, which incidentally had all stopped. I was worried about their returning in the future and about the change-over from one drug to the other. But the doctor assured me that there would be no problem stopping one and starting the other the same day. With some misgivings and recollection of my panic attack, I reluctantly agreed.

A few days later, feeling worried by the tingling in all my muscles probably caused by the change of drug, a trip to the bathroom at 7-30 am. took me passed the dayroom. To my surprise, a circle of old ladies was installed in the armchairs in the corner opposite the television. They were all knitting; all their paraphenalia of wool and pins were arranged beside them. I wondered how long they had been there. It was heartening to see that some chatting between the patients actually did go on.

Sitting waiting for the morning drug round, Olive touched my hand. Did I want to know who everyone was, she asked. She started with Violet aged about 55 with short grey hair, scantily dressed and with no teeth, pulling on a tab end she'd found in an ashtray. Turning round she caused a ripple of sniggering laughter amongst the seated patients. Slowly the reason became clear. Violet's nightdress was tucked up at the back revealing her buttocks to the assembled. A nurse seeing the comedy told her brusquely to go and put her dressing gown on and adjust her clothing. Violet refused.

"If you don't, you wont get a cup of tea after the drug round", the nurse said. Violet refused again and left. Five minutes later she was back - wearing her dressing gown.

The tingling all over my body had worsened into pain. Only constant movement and fidgetting brought any relief day or night. It was two weeks since the drug change-over. I was in hell. Time passed very slowly, but today was my next interview with the doctor.

In the interview room I told him my plight. He had little to offer. In agony I asked if I could lie on the floor. He agreed. There I rolled about trying to find relief. I could not go on, I told him, whilst he carried on the interview with my wife. At the end of the session I said I was going to change back to the original drug. If I did, he said I would probably be on it for the rest of my life and that he could not do any more. I am sure he thought that I was a failure, a wimp for not being able to carry on.

By mid-afternoon I was feeling much better. Just taking one triptafen had dispelled all the pain. (In retrospect I might have been able to carry on with the change-over if periodically I could have taken the odd triptafen; but no-one thought of this at the time).

In the coming days I realised how displeased the doctor was with me. He had lost all interest in my case and he did not confirm or discomfirm the diagnosis of C.F.S./M.E.

Not having seen Olive recently I caught up with her at coffee-time one morning. Feeling better now, I told her all about my ordeal. In reply she re-echoed all of her misgivings. After some thought I suggested, that maybe she would like to walk with me to the coffee shop on the campus. It was about a 200 metres round trip and a similar distance to that from her house to the shops. We could test out whether she could cope. She was very pleased and quietly agreed.

"You can be my toy boy" she glinted.

An hour later we were back after a hesitant trip. But Olive was full of renewed confidence. She had done it. The future did not seem so forbidding now.

Days passed, with the dayroom filled with the haze of cigarette smoke. Periodically Violet and Sheila would search the ash-trays for cigarette ends to smoke. Once one was found Sheila, a woman in her thirties and one of the most ill there, would relentlessly pace up and down the room with a vacant expression on her face.

When I first arrived I worried about how bizarre the patients would be. Only a few matched the usual stereotype. After a time, I was there long enough to see some people get better and leave; but leaving wasn't that easy. Not everyone looked forward to departure as I was to find out myself. The ward and its regime encouraged passivity, dependence and a feeling of safety and security.

One morning at about 10-30 a.m. I sat by Hilda and asked, what turned out to be a fatal question.
"How are you Hilda?" I said.
"Absolutely terrible" she replied.

I realised why no-one ever asked that question in there. Hilda, aged 81 had had depression and so was referred to this psychiatric hospital from an old people's home. Now she was being sent back. She had been on the ward for so long that she had forgotten what it was like at the home and dreaded the transfer. She complained of having no teeth, of looking terrible and having no presentable clothes. Her anxiety was overwhelming. She was twisting and writhing in agony in her seat. I tried to get her to relax; I called a nurse but he said he'd already tried to help her but failed. Nothing I did could console Hilda.

Eventually I had to move away because her pain was too much for me. No wonder you hardly ever saw nurses talking to patients. On reflection I wondered why no-one had thought to take Hilda on a day trip to re-acquaint her with her old residential home as a way of resolving her anxiety.

One breakfast time I happened to be sat next to Diane. She was about 45, very thin but quite attractive. Her hands shook as she incessantly smoked. Her problem had started 10 years before, when her husband died suddenly. Since then she went through periods of manic over-activity. She stayed out very late at night and at this time of the morning, 9a.m., was showily dressed in evening wear. This was not because she'd got up early but because she hadn't yet been to bed.

There was a bit of commotion as a dapper little man of about fifty came into the dining room. He was talking in a loud voice making comments and observations on people he saw. Diane's flashy evening dress caught his eye and he held forth.

"Who the hell do you think you are over there? Bloody Joan Collins, - with your fur-coat and glitzy dress. My God anyone'd think you were in Hollywood not a lunatic asylum". He was acid in his comments and nothing could stop him. With an aside from a nurse, she told me that he was an ex-patient. With that, all became clearer.

He went on to show everyone, who had stopped to see the drama, the little case he was carrying. It was for carrying woods for the game of green bowls, except that he had two bone-china figureens inside instead. He was so proud of them, he took them with him everwhere he went.

His diatribe faded gradually from earshot as he was quietly ushered out by a couple of nurses. Everyone sighed with relief, dreading being caught by his evil eye and savaged by his wit. I looked at Diane. She'd hardly turned a hair; she had just carried on smoking.

As the time of my own discharge home came nearer, I felt my fears about coping at home, growing. I was apprehensive about leaving hospital. Fantasies of having to rush back to the ward were kaleidoscopic in my mind. At least going home I could resume my sex life. (Behan and Bakheit, 1991) are right when they say libido is depressed in endogenous depression but not with C.F.S./M.E.

My wife arrived to collect me. As we left the building a chilling scream followed us.

"Let me go; take your hands off me" echoed down the corridor.

Nurses from all directions converged on a woman's bedroom. All I could think was 'God help her', she must be beside herself with distress.

I left hospital on the 3rd April 1987 and gradually on six triptafen a day my energy returned. Fear of the depression, suicidal fantasies and of never getting back to work were replaced by a positive outlook. I was finding that deep relaxation followed by reciting encouraging self-statements about my progress, my achievements and good things in my life, had a very pleasing effect on my mood.

With great relief and gratitude I started back to work on 13th May. I felt golden. The education authority in a very compassionate way agreed to me working half-time but on full salary for three months.

Everything was turning out fine with only one cloud on the horizon. At the start of the June holidays I mowed the lawns, and sprayed the roses with pesticide. It resulted in some worrying fatigue, which took ten days to clear. I should have taken more notice of this warning sign, but I didn't. I was a slow learner.

Through September I succeeded in working a longer day trying to avoid the possibility of having a cut in my salary. I thought I would feel a great loss of self-esteem if I'd had to take a cut. So full-time working was my goal. (In retrospect this was thinly veiled greed. It was to result in me eventually losing my job and salary altogether).

However the atmosphere was changing at work under the new principal psychologist. Many of his preferred practices diminished people's autonomy at work and consequently increased their workplace stress. I became most upset when 60 files I'd prepared for my work were demanded by the new principal for the use of other psychologists. One afternoon I spent an hour angrily carrying these files from my room to the proposed new shelving at the other end of the building. I took breaks and did not feel tired at all but it was an hours physical exertion. Within days a fatigue so great developed that I had to stay off work. I was dismayed. I had been doing so well. It was just an hours insignificant effort that had such devastating results.

After resting on sick leave for a few weeks in September 1987, I was well enough to return to work. Initially I coped very well, but gradually as fatigue mounted each day the work felt harder and harder. Anxiety about coping then became an increasing problem. Before having to interview teachers and children I would have to rest and relax in the car to counter these feelings. It was like walking in quicksand. Each struggle to cope deepened my dilemma. Eventually exhausted I had to take sick leave again. This tortured cycle was repeated many times. I am sure that your rationale becomes distorted. You cannot think straight. (In retrospect I should have rested until fit and then worked half-time or less for a year to get a stable work-pattern but I didn't conceive of this and my family and I had no contact with anyone who could better advise us. This is the purpose of this book. **Any C.F.S./M.E. sufferer should not struggle on trying to cope in this way.** It makes the illness infinitely worse as my unfolding story will show).

Then it happened. In November 1987 I'd been shopping in town for half an hour really enjoying myself. When I arrived home, fatigue grew for the rest of the day. The next morning I woke exhausted. I'd relapsed. Anxiety, panic attacks, suicidal ideas and heavy fatigue continued for days. I kept a diary of ever activity I did and the time spent on it. I paid myself 10 pence a day for each day achieved without a further relapse. This worked for a time but did not prevent relapse after relapse occurring. I was terrified of this continuing and being locked into this cycle for ever. I made a list of positive statements that I would read to cheer myself up. My wife was having to wash my hair now as I was too tired. I feared the phone ringing as it might be someone who would ask me to do something. I never said, "Can I help you?" as I had no energy to help anyone.

Massive self-control was required to rest and resist doing something for more than a few minutes, to avoid the incredible boredom. On a good day I did well managing this oscillation between rest, a few minutes activity, then rest again. I constantly thought about my life and how I'd arrived in this state of affairs again. What had I done wrong?

Eventually by late June 1988 I'd avoided a relapse for 45 days. I was really pleased with myself. I totalled up that I had relapsed 19 times so far; an appalling statistic. (See figure 1.2.1).

50

Figure 1.2.1 Relapses from July 1987 to January 1991.

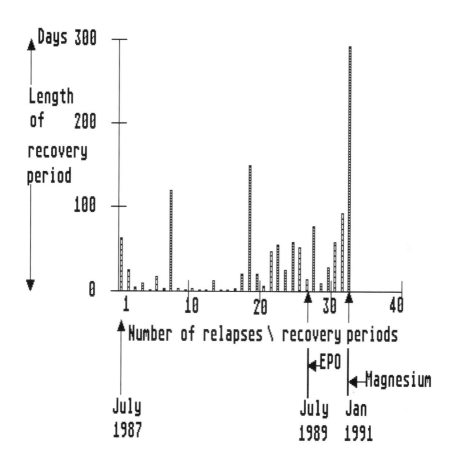

KEY: EPO = Evening Primrose Oil.

Through this term from May to July 1988 I worried how I would cope with giving up my job altogether and taking early retirement. My wife and I would lie awake in bed at 3 a.m. in the dead of night feeling very alone and deeply scared of what the future might hold for us. We feared poverty, homelessness, destitution, misery. It was frightening, unknown, uncharted; unpredictable. The day for my return to work came and went.

The awful process of losing my job and having to go on early retirement was set in motion. We would work and re-work our family finances trying to find the best way of managing with the impending halving of our income. I was to receive a retirement pension and invalidity benefit and the proceeds of a permanent health policy taken out in an hour of wisdom for just this eventuality.

The best support for my wife came from our friends from university days who frequently rang from different ends of the country to enquire of my progress. My great friend, a colleague from work was an immense support to me. These friends seemed to know instinctively how best to help us. They just listened and listened to our tale - giving little unsolicited advice and no criticism. They just seemed to calmly soak up our apprehension and anxieties. They allayed our fears and even though they were powerless to change anything, things did feel better after talking to them. We felt more fortified with resolve to continue to try to find the best way out of our dilemma.

I was feeling I must make as much effort as possible to get better, but was unsure how to do it. I was constantly despondent about being ill; angry that it was me; waking every morning to remember anew my predicament. Would I be doing this for the next forty years? The prospect was appalling.

JULY 1988, EARLY RETIREMENT.
In July 1988 there was a double whammy. In the same week, I attended my retirement party at work and, through the post received copies of my first published book, "Action Research In The Secondary School. The Psychologist As Change Agent", published by Routledge. It had taken ten years to produce. It was a week of much poignance. By now I had learnt to avoid anger and recriminations. I looked at the positive side of retirement; like having more time to spend on my interests instead of having to go to work.

However, reminders of my precarious health were ever-present.

One day in August 1988 I prepared the car to go on a caravan holiday; our first for some time. I pumped up the car tyres with a foot pump. That did it. Within hours I was feeling pulses of extreme anxiety, hot flushes, sensitivity to noise, and feared a relapse. I lay down, rested and waited. By the end of the day it was passing off. Thank God I had not relapsed, but I **resolved never to do any activity requiring physical exercise or effort ever again.** I had finally made the connection between exercise of my muscles and the onset of C.F.S./M.E. symptoms of extreme fatigue and relapsing. It had taken a long time to learn. I was just saddened that no-one in the medical profession had been knowledgeable enough to tell me this principle, unequivocally years ago.

At last we set off on holiday to the New Forest in our caravan and had an excellent time. Although restricted I was getting my life back bit by bit. I was really enjoying it. It was a pleasure to be alive. I thanked God every day for my deliverance. I felt golden again. In September I was doing so well that my G.P. suggested I try to reduce the dosage of the triptafen.

On six tablets per day i.e. 42 per week, I agreed to drop to 41 a week. A month later feeling no problems I reduced again to 40 a week. After two weeks, fatigue cut my daily period of being up and about, not lying down, from six hours to four hours per day and my ability to do clerical work from two to one hour a day. I felt a little disquiet. Then on the 5th October 1988 whilst in Birmingham my first relapse for months heralded a period of such misery and unhappiness, pain and despair I came very close to not surviving. It was to be the single most outstanding achievement of my life to get through it.

I had caused this relapse in trying to reduce the triptafen and now they were happening every few days or weeks. The pain was unrelenting except for odd islands of pleasure; like when I found a little note from my wife in my diary saying "I love you" or when my younger daughter came home from school. She would come upstairs to see me lying down in one of the bedrooms and relate to me all of her daily news. She probably did not realise that these, perhaps inconsequential acts to her, were peak experiences for me.

A relapse just before Christmas in December 1988 and unable to travel, ensured we as a family spent it alone. Few others spared our feelings as they described the wonderful time they were having. We felt like the only family in the world to have a problem.

As January 1989 progressed I improved, but was set back yet again after helping my elder daughter with her maths homework. It was another grim discovery. Not only physical but mental effort could cause a relapse. I had spent only a quarter of an hour thinking through a probability problem with her. I cried in rage at the injustice. I was at times having to lie down for 10 hours a day after sleeping for twelve. The boredom was crushing. A relative telephoned to say that now I'd given up my job, why wasn't I well. For her, logic dictated that the cause of my illness was not my job. It therefore must be my wife. The very person who was keeping me alive was now being blamed as the cause of my agony. The cruelty of this person, in saying this was beyond comprehension. I was beside myself with anger and despair.

A nasty comment may only take a moment to say and soon be forgotten by the perpetrator but have a long lasting effect on the victim.

With every relapse came a long period of readjustment; a coming to terms with the loss of activity and pleasure. It was a reactive depression. Sometimes the anguish and heavy leaden fatigue was so great that I could find no relief. There was no guarantee of recovery. I feared never improving. Suicide was becoming a very serious possibility. Only complete relaxation and clearing my mind of all thoughts and images whilst lying down gave any respite.

I was so desolate, locked into despair with the chill of loneliness that only chronic illness can bring, that I stood in the lounge and screamed so loud and for so long it resembled the shout of Alan Bates in the film of that name. In consequence I felt better, but nothing and no-one stirred in the street. It was as if I did not exist.

But my plan was building. I'd decided when, where, and how to do it. I wrote my farewell messages. Getting a phone-call every day to see how I was, I realised my wife was beginning to fear the worst; each day on her return never knowing what she might find. The prospect of unending misery with no hope of recovery was becoming too much. One day, life seemed so bleak and arid and comfort so far away that I resolved to do it that day; in an hour's time. All my fears of jeopardizing eternal life, of dying only to experience something worse, of breaking my promise to my wife; were overcome. I lay there on my bed. I had decided. All I had to do was to await the appointed time.

But as time passed, something unbelievable happened. Having made this momentous decision to end it all, having looked into the abyss, I began to feel strangely at peace; it was all over, no more struggle; no more pain and anguish. It was the end.

I enjoyed the serenity and gradually realised that perhaps I need not go just now. I could postpone it. Now I'd found an escape route I need only use it as an absolute last resort. I felt a little better and resolved to hang on a bit longer. At this time when things were very low, my wife talked of wanting to end the situation one way or another for herself. Such contemplation brought me close to giving up the struggle again; to a point beyond caring. Could it get any worse? However, this happened only once. That she should say this is a measure of **her** suffering. At this time, I marvelled at her fortitude and stamina, her optimism and good nature. I was very grateful that we were still together after all we had been through. Sometimes great good fortune, rubs shoulders with, co-exists with, moments of empty darkness. This strange melange made an indelible impression in my mind.

I made a special effort to avoid being negative, critical or morose but to praise and compliment her on all her endeavours, especially on the loving way she always supported me. She was there whenever the need arose and the greatest gift that I could bestow on her she said, was to return to good health, so that we might take up both our lives again. That became my principal endeavour. I realised that, if I was ever going to get well and for how ever long it took, I would need to maintain the loving strength of our family. I had to remember the needs of my wife and children as well as my own.

When on the rare occasions we did disagree I was so devoid of mental and physical reserves that I formulated a way of responding that was minimalist; the least costly. I discovered that the philosophy of an eye for an eye, getting you own back and thoughts of revenge are bankrupt. They may improve one's self-esteem for a while, because you have asserted yourself, but in the long term they are wasteful of personal energy and destructive of personal relationships.

I can understand why this principle has been morally superceded by the Christian ones of "love thy neighbour" and "turn the other cheek". The revenge mentality in a marital relationship is injurious to the aggrieved and likely to maintain or escalate the disagreement. In fact I have after much deliberation and many challenging experiences, realised that I have rediscovered the Christian philosophy of life; a philosophy that has been proved to be sustainable through the lives of millions of people across thousands of years.

Better to be as helpful as possible with your partner, than be angry and aggressive; to have sympathy and empathize with their situation and in a crisis, stay calm, not over-react and avoid making things worse by what you say or might do.

I would avoid periods when she or I was tired, in which to have analytical problem-solving discussions. I would choose a more optimal time.

I have realised that doing nothing may be the best course of action sometimes and as a last resort leavening the situation with some tactful humour may just defuse the crisis, giving everyone a breathing space.

It felt like trying to navigate in tricky waters; watching my own feelings and behaviour and its impact on the rest of the family.

Realising that we all have immense power over other people by how we respond to them, I resolved to adopt a simple strategy; to as far as possible be rewarding to everyone in my company, not just those in the family, so that they would, maybe come again; to talk and listen. Like it or not, I really was being refined in the furnace of affliction; life itself was forcing me to do it.

Most of the time when resting I would have my published book beside me. It was a symbol of a material achievement of mine. It served to remind me of my small successes in life. It helped me hang on and wait for better times.

But the relapsing carried on through the spring and summer of 1989. I listed the various causes. They included, walking, a lovely evening out to a restaurant for a meal, cooking, sex, proof reading, mental activity, talking too long, a bad night's sleep etc.

I listed all of the tiny events that I found rewarding. I constructed the day so that it was punctuated by rest and little rewards, like a cup of China tea, a special biscuit, a hug, looking at the family photo album, watching TV, a walk in the garden or looking at my computer and when less ill a walk to the shops. One of my favourite activities was to go to the multi-storey car park where I could leave the car and then walk, in a moment, to the coffee lounge at Beatties in Sutton Coldfield. I always tried to find someone to talk to.

(By now my eyes and brain were affected by the M.E. so that I could not read, write or compute without getting marked headaches and feeling awfully ill. Following the plot of TV programmes was a problem especially linking speech to the next visual scene. I would not make the connections between them).

I learnt to be pleased with just feeling well when it occurred. I gave myself little treats for small achievements.

I resolved to find pleasure in everything that happened to me and everything I did. No opportunity was to be wasted.

It took about 18 months from September 1989 to January 1991 and a number of prescriptions for new lenses for my glasses, before I could read without symptoms.

Between January and July 1989 the Permanent Insurance Company asked me to see various medical specialists, I suspected because they were querying the diagnosis of M.E. I saw a neurologist, psychiatrist and immunologist.

JULY 1989.
By the time I saw Professor Field, an expert in M.E., at Warwick University, I had managed to do 44 days without a relapse. He agreed that I had M.E. and put me on Evening Primrose Oil and fish oil (the same as Efamol) and suggested that my family drink filtered tap water. He had the theory that pollutants in the water over-load the body's immune system in people with M.E. This interview was to be a watershed for me.

In August we managed to go on holiday in our caravan to Northamptonshire near Princess Diana's ancestral home, Althorp.

It was a little irksome hearing about all of our relatives and friends going abroad for their holidays. No-one thought to consider our feelings or chagrin at not doing the same - but deep down we ignored this insensitivity, being grateful we were getting a holiday at all. For sometime I had felt the nagging ache of being apart from society, excluded, isolated by this chronic illness. Everywhere you look in the neighbourhood and especially on TV, everyone seems to be fit and well and getting on with their exciting lives. My ex-colleagues at work were now earning twice my income. However, I eventually stopped comparing myself to others and only compared myself to the time when I was more seriously ill. In recent months I had recovered a great deal. I was improving, I was getting my life back alittle. We were feeling happier; that's what really mattered.

My family looked round the stately home of Althorp whilst I lay down in the car for an hour and just joined them in the coffee shop. In fact, I lay down most of the holiday, but I didn't mind. I was out and about, seeing new places; well, lying down in new places! I was grateful to be able to do what I could.

In September 1989 we decided to buy a new caravan because my youngest daughter had out-grown the little bunk bed she used. I had gone 80 days since the last relapse. I was feeling less diffident about the future, but still unable to read, write or use the computer.

Buying the caravan generated some anxiety and obsessional thoughts - but these were controlled by using a relaxation tape regularly two or three times a day.

But the excitement and pleasure of doing jobs on the caravan resulted in a relapse. I was back to the beginning again. I had done 83 days.

As I improved I realised that this recovery was more rapid than previous ones. I put this down to the effects of the Evening

Primrose Oil. In December came another relapse but it turned out to be the most inoccuous one I'd ever had. (A month earlier the Permanent Insurance Company stopped paying out on my policy.

They decided that I was suffering from a psychiatric condition and therefore invoked the exclusion clause in the policy. This was a great financial shock which added further stress to the family at this difficult time).

CHAPTER 3. SOME IMPROVEMENT.

CARAVANNING TO WYTHALL.
March 1990 was the next relapse, but I managed to recover enough to go caravanning in the Easter holidays.

Caravanning has enhanced my family's life for years, both when I was a boy with my parents and with my own family.

By April 1990 I was able to be up and about for two hours without resting, walk or do physical tasks for only quarter of an hour per day, but I needed to lie down for seven and a half hours per day. Dare I go caravanning just a month after my last relapse?

We decided on visiting a site near to our home - about 50 minutes towing time away. We planned to go to Wythall, a village south of Birmingham, well placed for visits to the Warwickshire countryside, Stratford on Avon, Leamington Spa and Coventry.

It is a Caravan Club site open all the year round with nearly a hundred pitches. The week before intending to travel my wife, and our two daughters washed and packed the van. I did one quarter hour job per day, first checking the external lights, the car, the van tyres and the mains electric. I was strict about doing no more than 15 minutes per day. If I did more, I risked relapsing and being set back yet again. The most testing time was to be the hitching up and towing off. The family pulled the caravan into the correct position whilst I rested, only taking part to actually hitch up, plug in the electrics and put on the stabilizer. All that just took five minutes; I timed it. That left 10 minutes activity to spend in the rest of the day.

Towing was no problem and taking just 50 minutes was well within my two hours. The next hurdle would be the pitching of the van. To avoid having to push and pull the van I backed it into position using the car. I put on the gas and connected up the main's electricity whilst the girls fetched the water. I sat supervising in the garden chair! Again my part cost just five minutes of activity. We had made it. I then had to lie down resting for much of the remainder of the day. I had five minutes activity left which I would use for a stroll round the site in the evening.

My only fear was that some unforeseen problem in the van would arise, and cost me time and effort to fix.

However whilst the family went out to explore that afternoon I rested. I was glad to be on holiday, glad to be experiencing a different scene and glad to be alive. I enjoyed lying down in the van. We chose a Swift Corvette because you can lie down without having to set the beds up. There was something new to look at compared with resting at home. I watched the caravanners do their chores around the site through the windows and sometimes watched T.V. Surprising when I noticed, was the quality of the workmanship in the manufacture of the van. All the grain of the wood panelling matched for each of the cupboard doors. The walls were interesting because of the texture they exhibited.

Resting in the van was a warm cosy experience. I was thankful I only had M.E. and nothing terminal. At least with rest it is possible to make some recovery from M.E. in a couple of years. I just had to be patient.

With the return of the family we had a cup of speciality tea and enjoyed the rest of the afternoon. Often after reading the Sunday papers my wife would give me an account of the best stories; very enjoyable.

However the next day just before breakfast, my elder daughter burst out of the toilet compartment wrapped only in a towel complaining that the floor was flooded. We all thought she must have been careless washing herself and splashed the water around, but on looking, we found the carpet saturated. There was a plughole in the floor and dirty water was welling up through it.

My immediate worry was that solving this problem would take longer than a quarter of an hour. At first I thought water from the wash basin was leaking, but then I went outside and inspected the van under the toilet compartment floor. There I found the shower compartment outlet pipe. This and the one from the kitchen sink were the two outlet pipes in the outside wall of the van. What had happened was the waste bucket was full and the waste water had backed up the shower compartment pipe to the floor. Two minutes and the problem was solved. We just had to mop up the dirty water and dry the carpet.

In the afternoon we all went to Ragley Hall, the 17th century stately home of the Marquess of Hertford, not far away. The house dates from 1680 and was designed by Robert Hook. Of course I had to go and wait in the tea-room whilst the family looked round the house. I had used up my quarter of an hour activity with the flood. However the tea-room was charming and the tea splendid. Watching the visitors choose tables, select cakes and drink their tea was entertaining. When she returned, my wife described to me all the facets of the house and furniture in great detail.

The next day's activity was taken up with emptying the porta-potti. Because of the effort involved I had to bring the car to the caravan door, position the elsan in the boot and drive to the emptying point. To carry it would have been too risky. Completing that task was the activity of the day.

Breakfast-time seemed to have a strange attraction for problems. Just finishing washing again our elder daughter lifted the tip-up wash-basin in the toilet compartment to empty the water, where upon it gushed out of the back panel and all over her legs. She was having no luck and here was yet another problem for me, making demands on my time. On the back of the basin were the instructions for removing it from the wall unit. This involved springing two lugs out of their holes. This done, the back compartment leading down to the plug hole could be seen. A finger in the plug hole revealed a mass of clogged and matted hair. It was this that was causing the obstruction. This removed and the basin replaced all worked well again, but we realised that if anyone washed their hair in this basin the plughole needed to be cleared afterwards. That was 10 minutes gone!

The afternoon was spent visiting the tea-room at Baddesley Clinton country house. The history of Baddesley begins long before the 13th century. It is now National Trust property.

However this was to prove an embarassing visit for my wife. She was walking in the hall in shoes with a modest heel when an officious attendant appeared from behind a table with a pair of what seemed to be bright blue crinkly plastic bags. She asked my wife to put these on instead of her shoes to protect the floors from the heels. She reluctantly agreed and proceeded to look and feel foolish exploring the house in this foot-wear to the amusement of all the self-righteous ladies who had thought to come in flat shoes.

By the afternoon of our last day, no problems had occurred to rob me of my activity time so I spent it looking round the shop at Coughton Court, another country house situated on the out-skirts of the old Forest of Arden two miles from Alcester and 18 from Birmingham. I loved looking through the nature books, tea towels and china. I enjoyed perusing the honey, preserves and speciality tea shelves. I don't usually buy much, though; perhaps some fancy-writing paper and envelopes. Then it was back to the cosiness of our van for a cup of tea.

Thinking ahead to the trip home, I reckoned I'd have to empty the toilet, hitch up the van and unhitch at home in my 15 minutes.

All went well with the rest of the family helping. Although I had used up my time as I pulled off the site, I knew it would take only a moment to de-couple at home. I drove home basking in the pleasure that I had made it on holiday and that from now on, if I didn't relapse, things would get easier on subsequent trips. The holiday served to assuage my guilt at doing so little in the way of household jobs at home for the family; I felt less of a drone; less useless.

JANUARY 1991.
It was in January 1991 that I made a mistake in judging how much activity I could manage. Walking for an hour followed by writing for an hour caused another relapse. I had lived for 291 days without one; nearly a year; the best progress yet.

As can be imagined, the adjustment to lying down and resting for most of every day again took an age. All of the old symptoms were back. I was weary of them but now could see the prospect of better health in front of me if only I could solve the problem of relapsing.

Through-out my illness my parents tried very hard to help me. When well enough I would visit them during the week for a day. Unfortunately in their anxiety to help they generated an avalanche of advice; a common reaction of family's in trying to cope with chronic illness.

This advice transmogrified itself into what felt like criticism. Was I on the right diet, shouldn't I spend all my savings now, as you don't live forever.

I have learnt from my reading about chronic illness, how it can wreck relationships not only with your spouse and children but also with your other relatives as well. It requires insight to realise that people's behaviour is motivated by a desire to help the invalid and this can generate much unsolicited advice that sounds like criticism. This serves to help reduce people's own uncomfortable anxieties, feelings of impotence and lack of control over the problem.

65

These relatives visited me one day. I was feeling very bad and could not cope with anyone phoning me. They might ask me to do something. This always caused a burst of anxiety. So I left the phone off the hook. These visitors had tried to phone me and finding it engaged, feared the worst. They rushed round to see me and on finding that the phone was off the hook berated me for it. They said it was illegal to do this. The telephone operator however, confirmed that it was not. I was very ill. I didn't need a telling off.

I realised later that this was an indication of their own anxieties.

At times I tried to assert myself and explain how upsetting too much advice can be. It was very difficult, but as I improved and I was able to be more assertive I felt more comfortable.

In fact it is very difficult to be assertive again after being ill. A special step by step program is needed aimed at incrementally changing your own behaviour as well as that of those around you whose dominant behaviour helps maintain you in submissiveness.

Some relatives can go to extraordinary lengths to protect themselves from the pain of the anxieties generated by the invalid's illness. For me, some would not even accept that I was ill. They said I was just tired, that was all, even though I was lying down 22 hours a day, week in week out.

I once had the chance to help a colleague with such a problem. His daughter was telephoning him from university relating her anxieties and problems. She had only recently recovered from a life-threatening illness. In trying to advise her, she became angry eventually ringing off in exasperation, only to repeat the episode a few days later. My friend asked me for my view. Judging from my own position as an invalid, I suggested he should just quietly listen to her story and to avoid interrupting with advice, but towards the end of the conversation to **ask her** how she might improve her situation (called Socratic questioning) and to agree with any reasonable suggestions that she made.

My colleague tried this approach and reported back that it had worked. It had removed all the animosity from the conversation. His daughter was ringing off in a much more positive mood.

Sometimes people do not want advice, they just want someone to listen to them.

The invalid has to be strong and tell their relatives how they want to be helped; but this is easier said than done.

My progress was real though. As figure 1.2.1 shows, I suffered a total of 34 relapses between July 1987 and January 1991 generating 34 recovery periods.

Only the first to the 33rd recovery periods are shown on the graph. The 33rd lasted 291 days before I relapsed again on the 4th January 1991. I started taking Evening Primrose Oil and fish oil (Efamol) on the 26th July 1989 at around the time of the 28th relapse. It can be seen that this treatment is associated with longer recovery periods. These more recent recovery periods are longer and gave me enough of the pleasures of life to maintain my motivation to keep trying to get as well as possible and stop relapsing.

The 34th recovery period is now at April 2008 and still continuing. I pray that it will.

The magnesium injections started on the 21st June 1991 and continued to 4th January 1996. They are associated with the longest recovery period that has occurred (see figure 1.3.1).

THE INSURANCE OMBUDSMAN.

By June 1991 I was in touch with the Insurance Ombudsman about my permanent health policy.

After becoming ill in 1980 with pneumonia I decided to take out a permanent health insurance policy which would pay nearly the equivalent of my salary if I was so incapacitated as to be unable to work, in the future. In July 1988 I did have to retire.

In October 1982 I took out such a policy with the Permanent Insurance Company (PIC) a member of the Medical Sickness Group, 7/10 Chandos Street, Cavendish Square, London W1A 2LN. Because of my previous illness of depression they put an exclusion clause in the policy saying that:

"No benefit shall be payable in respect of incapacity due to or arising from anxiety state, neurosis, depression or psychosis."

The Permanent Insurance Company paid out on my policy from July 1988 until November 1990 when they invoked an exclusion clause in my policy and stopped paying. It was due to be paid until I was aged 60 or until the illness resolved and I could return to work. I took my case to the Insurance Ombudsman to see if he could help restore my policy. The following story relates my experience.

After reducing my tablets considerably I suffered a relapse in 1984 and 1986 involving not depression but gross fatigue. On both occasions I made a good recovery on my normal dose of triptafen. In June 1986 I became aware of M.E. and the symptoms seemed to fit my illness perfectly. Excessive fatigue, muscle twitching, sensitivity to noise, light, heat, cold and caffeine were all part of my illness. At the same time I saw my psychiatrist who said he'd also become aware of M.E. and thought this was the only explanation for my illness.

In January 1988 I had a test for M.E. carried out by the M.E. Association and that was positive.

The insurance company sent me to see a neurologist in December 1988 who thought my illness could be caused by anxiety and depression. Notice we have here a neurologist making a psychiatrist diagnosis. However he did think that there was a problem with my immune system. My psychiatrist did not agree with him and in February 1989 reported to the insurance company that my illness "had no psychiatric cause."

At the instigation of my insurance company I saw an immunologist at East Birmingham Hospital who agreed with the M.E. diagnosis, as did my G.P.and Dr.H. who saw me in June 1988 for my DFEE (Department for Education and Employment) pension.

In July 1989 I saw Professor Field of The Naomi Bramson Medical Trust at Warwick University privately and again on his test for M.E. I was positive. He prescribed Evening Primrose Oil. I have been on it ever since.

The PIC decided not to pay out on my claim because of the exclusion clause for psychiatric illness quoting the neurologist's report. After contacting the Ombudsman the PIC agreed to a second psychiatric opinion and after seeing this second psychiatrist on 28th January 1991 still refused to pay my claim.

My psychiatrist who has known me for many years says the illness is not psychiatric and a second psychiatrist who saw me for one hour says that there was no depression but some anxiety possibly due to M.E. We have not seen his report but the Ombudsman's assistant told me its contents. The company have not yet sent us to see an M.E. expert or incidently sent us copies of any of the medical reports. It is clear from the medical literature that M.E. is an organic illness. Professor Behan of the Southern General Hospital Glasgow has been engaged in a million pound research project on M.E. and has been able to remove the virus from the cells of M.E. patients.   Undoubtedly there are psychological symptoms in M.E. such as anxiety and depression but they are by-products of the illness and it is excessive fatigue that stops me working.

Another reason for the company's refusal to pay my claim is that I am on anti-depressants and therefore they say I must be depressed. It is widely reported in the medical literature that tricyclic anti-depressants are most beneficial for M.E. patients as well.

Not satisfied with the response of the PIC I resolved to contact the Insurance Ombudsman (31 Southampton Row, London WC1B 5HJ). which I did in November 1990. He said I must present my case to the chief executive of the company first. I did this to no avail. The company did not reverse their decision.

They still failed to send copies of the doctors' reports to my G.P., so I was unclear as to what they were saying about me.

I rang the Ombudsman's assistant in July 1991 and he told me the contents of doctors' reports over the phone. This was the first time I had heard these. He also said that I had a good case against the PIC and that the underwriter at PIC dealing with my case also had agreed with this view over the phone.

We were told the Ombudsman's office was just awaiting a letter from the PIC agreeing to their judgement that my claim was justified. The PIC never sent that letter. The next thing we heard was in a letter from the Ombudsman himself on 7th August 1991 rejecting my claim and coming down on the side of the PIC.

This was a complete reversal of decision, between his assistant and the Ombudsman himself. **He said he believed M.E. existed and decided that his job was to judge whether I had M.E. or depression. He decided I had depression, saying the evidence**

against me was quite strong namely that I was on anti-depressants.

The Ombudsman agreed that my G.P., the DFEE doctor and the neurologist had found in my favour, (even though the neurologist had diagnosed anxiety depression and an immunological disorder).

He ignored the testimony of the two psychiatrists both of whom said there was no depression.

The Ombudsman would not comment on the opinions of his assistant or the PIC underwriter given over the phone. He also ignored the fact that anti-depressants are a treatment for M.E. as well as depression.

On 27th September 1991 the Ombudsman finally found against me. I should not have agreed to see medical specialists until the company agreed in writing to send a copy of the report to your G.P.

If I had depression, being treated with antidepressant would resolve it. But I was still too ill to work even with anti-depressants. Therefore I must have some disorder other than depression - something on top of or besides depression. This is diagnosis by elimination.

In an article by Christine Stopp entitled "M.E. sufferers forced to battle with insurers" published in the Sunday Independent on 27th June 1993, it was reported that a number of other M.E. sufferers were having the same difficulty as myself.

The M.E.Association are now collecting a list of people experiencing this problem.

MEASURES OF RECOVERY.

Figure 1.3.1 shows the very gradual recovery of capacity for physical activity and writing. It starts on 5th January 1991, the beginning of the last and longest recovery period. Remember I was taking the medication triptafen and Efamol before the magnesium treatment started on 21st June 1991. The triptafen and Efamol treatments are still continuing. Before the magnesium treatment started, I had a test for magnesium deficiency which was negative.

The measure called "physical activity" on the graph was either walking, washing up, laying the dinner table, occurring over a day in separate sessions but definitely did not include energetic activity like vacuuming the carpets or mowing the lawns.

The measure "writing" was either totally writing or desk work. Again this activity was performed over a day in separate sessions. It is clear from the graph that I could maintain writing for much longer in the day than physical activity. An increase in either activity only occurred after the previous increase had been easily tolerated for some time; usually weeks.

However, looking at figure 1.3.2 with a larger scale at the points on the graph from day 168 when the magnesium treatment started, there is an abrupt change in rate of progress for writing from 129 minutes (day 273) to 160 minutes (day 287).

It would appear that the magnesium treatment took some time before its effect was apparent. It may be that the magnesium treatment effect was delayed, in my case, for about 3 months.

Looking at figure 1.3.2 the change in rate of progress between

72

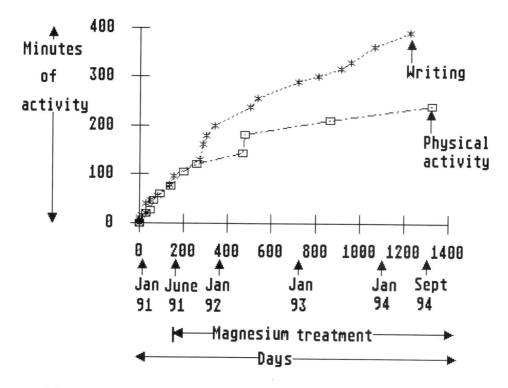

Figure 1.3.1 Graph of recovery of writing and physical activity.

points 129 to 160 minutes is marked. It is about a 25 per cent improvement.

However, at the time the magnesium treatment (injections) started, subjectively, I felt a great improvement in the sensations in my muscles. Almost immediately after the first injection the heavy leaden feeling when tired, disappeared. It is possible that without the Efamol or magnesium treatment my recovery would not have been so good. Some C.F.S./M.E. patients do not experience this month by month, year by year progress. For me I hope it is still continuing.

Both triptafen and Efamol have had a delayed effect with my C.F.S./M.E. and this might be also the case for the magnesium treatment.

Research into the effects of both Efamol and magnesium often only measure their effects over a very short period, usually only weeks but rarely longer than 6 months. Future evaluation, I would suggest needs to be conducted over a longer period, more like a year and with combinations of treatments.

It may be that the positive improvement I have seen is because the Efamol and magnesium were taken for a long period **simultaneously**.

Figure 1.3.2. Graph of recovery of writing only.

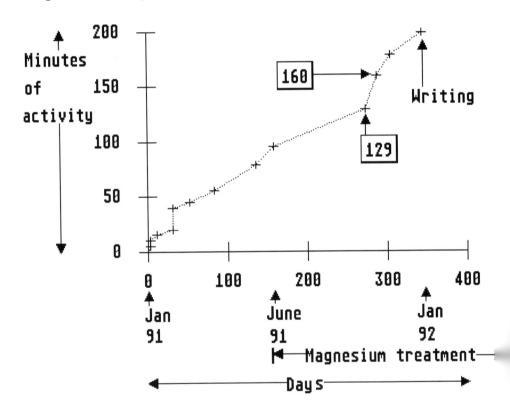

TO NORMANDY (AUGUST 1991).

By August 1991 I was well enough to embark on the family's first foreign holiday for many years.

Caravanning in France for a month may seem a crazy ambition for someone who is chronically ill, but this is just what we decided to do. I greatly feared making my illness worse and being ill abroad, but I knew how much pleasure and anticipation the family had in looking forward throughout the year to our trip.

We aimed to keep the holiday as stress-free as possible by planning it with plenty of short tows, stop-overs and rest. My trepidation was worst the night before we set off. I was not sure whether I would succeed or not.

My wife had booked all the camp-sites in England and France using the advance booking service of the Caravan Club so that our sites in France were paid for already.

All packed and ready to go I was relaxing on the penultimate evening, only to suddenly realise that it was the first time we would be using the electrics on a French camp-site. I made a quick phone call to my father who had caravanned in France before to discover whether there were any problems with this. There were. You needed a special continental plug for French sites and worse, the French wire up their system in at least two ways causing you to need a polarity tester to test the caravan 13 amp sockets for their polarity. I did not have a continental plug or a polarity tester. We decided to buy them on the way. After an initial panic, we felt more relaxed.

My recovery from C.F.S./M.E. was such that I could now walk or be active for just 1 hour 15 minutes a day. I had to time every activity to make sure I did not exceed the total for that day.

On our first morning I lay down until the caravan was ready to be hitched up. It was manoeuvred off the drive and hitched up. It took just 6 minutes. The lights were checked and we were off. We followed the A446 from Sutton Coldfield on to the M42, M40 and A4095 to Bladon and the Caravan Club site there.

The weather was brilliant and the towing easy. (Obviously sitting down when driving does not count for me as activity). My wife had booked us in at Bladon and all that remained to be done was to pitch the van, link up the electrics and turn on the gas. All this was done in 13 minutes, bringing my total to 19. I was well inside the total allowed, namely 75. Because it was such a short tow the afternoon was free. We found a caravan supplier and bought a polarity tester and plug.

The afternoon was spent walking in the beautiful village of Woodstock and relaxing over a cup of afternoon tea. We loved this time together giving us the opportunity to talk at length to each other. This walk cost 43 minutes making 62 in all. That day, I had time in hand.

Next day we towed on to Rookesbury Park Caravan Club site near Portsmouth. In the afternoon we reconnoitred the ferry terminal ready for the following day.

We aimed to take the car ferry from Portsmouth to Caen in Normandy and to do it necessitated rising at 5-30 am. I was a bit worried about having the energy to get through the day. It took 10 minutes to hitch up the van and in a short time we were towing on to the boat. The weather was warm and calm - just what you want for a channel-crossing. Once aboard I found our cabin and aimed to lie down and rest for the 5 hours of the crossing. I wished I could have walked round, exploring the boat but the fear of using up my time or getting too tired, kept me in the cabin. I had used 20 minutes so far that day. The air below decks was stifflingly hot until I discovered the air conditioning switch. I lay down dozing, thinking and worrying about finding the site and pitching in the time I had left that day (55 minutes). Was it all worth it?

However the time seemed to pass quickly, punctuated by coffee, lunch and a wash.

Driving off the ferry at Caen was no problem and we soon found the route to Benouville and "Hautes Coutures" our camp-site. My activity started with paying for the site electricity in advance, being shown to our pitch and manoeuvring the van into position.

The van pitched, I hooked up the electrics and tried out my polarity tester. I selected the correct plug. Pitching had taken 31 minutes and I still had the toilet to set up and locate the emptying point. That completed, I had run over time to 86 minutes; 11 too much. I had over done it. I was in dread that I would suffer as a consequence. However I did not feel tired but decided to lie down for the remainder of the day. I needed to lie down for 5 hours per day and consequently had to forego the pleasures of exploring the site, shop and bar with the family. But at least we had arrived and were settled.

I felt tremendously pleased with myself for succeeding in the day's accomplishments. Today was probably going to be the most demanding day and I had got through it. The day ended with the most horrendous rainstorm.

However in the morning we woke to bright sunshine. Enjoying a warm shower took only 15 minutes of my activity time. Then I had to lie down whilst everyone else was out in the sun. After lunch in brilliant sunshine we set off for the golden beaches of Riva Bella outside Ouistreham near Caen. Bedecked with half naked oiled bodies and parasols, the beach was a panorama of colour. Day after glorious day, each afternoon we soaked up the sun on shimmering sands.

For a change one day we decided to visit another seaside town, St.Aubin. Parking was very limited so we stopped in an area reserved for cars unloading boats on to the beach. There were other cars there so we thought it would not hurt to join them.

However we were apprehensive and whilst on the beach continued to watch our parking space. Half an hour later panic swept over us as we saw a gendarme arrive and start questioning the motorists.

Quick as a flash we packed up on the beach and scurried back to the car, heads down and eyes averted, dreading the gaze and attention of the policeman. The other cars were all getting tickets written out, but for us, perhaps because we were British, he had only a rye smile. We drove off politely vowing never to park illegally again. It just was not worth the worry.

The coming days were spent sunbathing and shopping in the open marketplace for food for our own gourmet meals. We bought carrolet - fillets of plaice, cabillaud - medallions of cod, crevettes - prawns, peaches, plums and melon. What pleasure we had in these purchases. I was beginning to really relax now; worries subsiding, I was truly enjoying the holiday for the first time. (I remember thinking that I was glad I had not gone through with my suicide plan and that I must treasure these memories to sustain me if I ever felt that bad again).

Special treats were our weakness. In Benouville there was a boulangerie and patisserie which sold beautiful cakes, from tarte aux pommes (apple) et creme anglaise to pain aux raisin and tarte aux fraises (strawberry). Our afternoon tea was greatly enhanced by these little confections.

That night we went to La Glycine restaurant in Benouville and had Salade Nicoise, supreme de poulet (chicken) and creme caramel. All for 65 Francs. Brilliant!

Not to be missed in Normandy is a visit to the Bayeux Tapestry dating from William the Conqueror and depicting the 1066 Battle of Hastings. For me with M.E. there was a dearth of seats to help cope with all the queueing. There was a great deal of pictorial information to view before getting to the actual tapestry itself.

Whilst I sat down, my wife went ahead and worked out the best way for me to see the most of the exhibits. It was a delight to see and was well worth the visit.

Equally resplendent was the Basilica at Lisieux, again not far from Caen. It was built in memory of Theresa Martin later canonized after her death in 1897, and is a most magnificent building. Begun in 1929 it is decorated with exquisite mosaics and stained glass windows. The monument is of breath-taking splendour.

Also you have to find time for some other sights in Normandy (a region famous for its apples, cider and Calvados brandy) namely the richly modelled houses of Deauville, the cathedral at Caen and the chateau at Fontaine-Henry.

One evening by chance we met a garrulous effusive French lady, Sylviane, at the bar, who on finding we could converse a little in French proceeded to give us her life story. We came to greatly enjoy these conversations over a drink each evening. The husband, son and daughter of Sylviane were all introduced to us.

However, we had to forego one evening. We had just been for a meal at a restaurant in Riva Bella, where our daughters ate mussels in the salad. Some years ago they had had food poisoning from mussels the last time we were in France.

It was not food poisoning this time, but food allergy to the mussels, that made them ill until 3 am in the morning. Back and forth I had to trek to the toilet block in the dead of night cleaning up. At the same time I worried about getting over-tired and relapsing myself. After a restless night's sleep, the morning brought much improvement to our daughters. But we have decided, they must not have mussels again.

As the conclusion of our stay at Hautes Coutures approached I began to get concerned about towing off, boarding the car ferry and driving home. I need not have worried, all went well and we arrived home safely without mishap. It looks as though, it is fortunately the way of the world, that most of the time, most things go reasonably well.

It goes without saying that I was hugely pleased that I had succeeded in achieving this holiday. It provided lovely memories that will give me a great deal of pleasure throughout the coming year. C.F.S/M.E. is not necessarily the end of the world. Caravanning offers an excellent way to go on holiday with great flexibility for the chronically ill or disabled. Much of what you do is under your own control.

We were now looking forward to many more such holidays and hope that this story will inspire other sufferers to take up caravanning, especially to the relatively close and rather under-rated region of Normandy.

JANUARY 1992.

Increasingly now I was living a "working" routine; getting up soon after the rest of the family and working on writing articles. It provided a daily purpose; a goal. In fact, after chronic illness or disability you have to find new goals in life for yourself. Once finished I would send these articles off to magazines.

Many were rejected initially but nearly all were published eventually. I just kept an eye open for likely receptive magazines.

The most exciting event was when one magazine accepted my article and sent a photographer round to our house to photograph the family. This news galvanized my teenage daughters into action, making-up and practising poses for the camera. It was as if their modelling careers were about to start. When the photographer did arrive, it was exactly like you see on TV. He had us posturing in one position and then in another, inside the caravan and then outside. The neighbours were intrigued as all of this went on in the driveway in front of our house.

It was around January 1992 that I started feeling ill just after mid-morning and mid-afternoon.   I feared it was the return of depression but the symptoms were not quite the same. Monitoring their progress through the day I discovered that they disappeared completely about 30 minutes after a meal. Eating food at about 10-30 a.m. and 3-00 p.m. solved the problem completely. It was hypoglycaemia - or low blood glucose that was causing the problem. Over the ensuing months it gradually resolved of its own accord.

This episode indicates how the symptoms of C.F.S./M.E. come and go, change and vary.

There was a similar story for headaches and eye ache caused by reading or writing.

However, it was during January 1992 that a past colleague of mine rang me. She was an educational psychologist who was engaged in some private work. She was getting inundated with so many requests - she asked me whether I would like to take on a case. It was a girl with a spelling problem.

I immediately said no; I had not seen a case for about five years. It was impossible. I could not do it.   The thought of it had drenched me in anxiety. But it did get me thinking. I rang her back and asked if I could phone her for a case in a few months time when I was ready to try to do one. She agreed.

So, I then set about relearning all my working skills. I bought a updated intelligence test for children and systematically practised it and other tests,   on my children for over a month.   My confidence built the more I did.

By March '92 I was ready to phone a headteacher who had promised his help in July 1988 if I ever needed it. I asked him if I could visit his school and with the parent's permission practise testing a normal cooperative child. I explained the background to my request. He immediately agreed and we set a date.

As the day drew closer the anxiety mounted. Constantly I was asking myself if I could cope with the two and a half hours it would take. I stiffened my resolve and confidence by remembering that I could now do over 3 hours writing without a break. This was the closest simulation I could get to the actual testing situation.

Every few hours I used cognitive behavioural techniques I had learnt from psychology and relaxation to control the anxiety. They worked brilliantly. Knowing these techniques was proving to be a great advantage in managing my illness myself.

On the morning of the day, my wife gave me a send off, recalling how it was like old times, before I had C.F.S./M.E. I dressed smartly as if doing it for real.

I parked the car, met the head and then the child, a girl of about 10 years. We sat down in a cosy little room with a table and chairs. I put her at ease with talk about any pets she had. I began to relax; it was like old times for sure. It was a pleasure to be using my old skills again. It was a golden moment.

At the end of the session I had coffee with the head and discussed my findings. All had gone well and I departed. I had done it; the first time in five years. I remembered a story my mother had told me about a middle-aged neighbour who had become very ill with a stroke. It took him five years to recover, to get off invalidity benefit on to unemployment pay and then back into a job of work. For the first time I dared to think this might happen to me. Maybe I could get back some more of my life.

Back home I rested all the remainder of the day just in case I had any symptoms. My confidence grew as with each hour I continued to feel well. I was filled with a great feeling of gratitude, happiness and satisfaction. My self-esteem improved and I more easily began to describe myself as a psychologist.in private practice! It sounds better than chronically ill and unemployable.

Discovering that anyone on Invalidity Benefit (now Incapacity Benefit) can apply to do paid work without losing benefit, if it can be construed as therapeutic, was a little triumph. I discussed this with my G.P. and told her of my recent achievement in practising testing. She agreed to the proposal and so did the Department of Social Security. It was brilliant.

In fact as this recovery period grew, 479 days so far, I was experiencing little bursts of pleasure and exhilaration when lying down resting; as though my whole system was recovering.

As my health improved, still unable to risk doing energetic chores like vacuuming or gardening, I looked for easy ways of helping the family. I realised that just being around to talk and listen was very useful. I took pleasure in doing everyone's odd jobs that were easier for me to do because of my flexible schedule and having more time. I would make phone-calls, make appointments and shop for obscure items. It was another useful way of enhancing my role at home. I tried to be a family facilitator. As my computer and computing skills came in handy for helping with homework assignments, I used to lie on the bed calling out instructions to my daughters for working on the word processor.

Teaching my elder daughter to drive turned out to be very worthwhile. Almost everyday we went out practising in the car round the town and country lanes. From time to time characterstic headaches would occur which forced me to have to give up all reading, writing and computing.

I discovered that refraining from such work for a few weeks was the best way of resolving them. Nevertheless, it was soul destroying to be back doing very little but resting all day long.

When this happened, I found that, happily, I could still walk for about an hour without a break if I walked in a totally relaxed unhurried fashion. Doing this every day regardless of the weather, I discovered was a surprising source of pleasure. The slow comfortable rhythm allowed my thoughts to meander about, musing on whatever came to mind. I grew to look forward to this time and maintained it even when I was again able to do academic or clerical work.

Surprising also were the repeated encounters with neighbours to whom I had rarely spoken before. Later, these outings gave me the confidence to take the bus to Sutton Coldfield town centre. In the past I had avoided such trips because of the fear of having to wait for buses and running out of energy before I could get home. The high regularity of the bus service and my timing of each part of the journey gave me the confidence to travel. This opened up another source of happiness; meeting people on the bus. I almost invariably started up the conversation with whoever I was sat next to, whether it was a pensioner, young mother or teenager. I have never had my attempts at conversation rejected. In every case I have enjoyed hearing about someone else's life in exchange for some proffered self-disclosure on my part. Life even as a chronic invalid was continually surprising me. I have learnt from my experiences to be ready and open, to enjoy all of the little pleasures that might, by luck, come my way. Everyday became a gamble; a game of chance. From where would my next small scintillation of delight come I wondered?

Once in the town centre, as an alternative to shopping, was to sit and just watch the people; they were fascinating especially the women. Make-up, hairstyles, fashion and natural beauty make most women more interesting than expensive works of art. It is curious how, being in a secure and loving relationship gives you the freedom to genuinely admire the qualities in women without suffering the risks of getting involved.

I reflected that when working before I retired, it was like being the gardener in a beautiful park, but working so hard that he never noticed the flowers.

I had lost my health, my career, my work colleagues and half my income, but as my C.F.S./M.E. improved I was beginning to build a new life and I appreciated what I already had, a wife, children, family, a home, friends and my computer which has gone from a hobby to providing alternative income.

In my regular weekly routine of visiting the Nationwide Building Society, Sutton Coldfield reference library and the United Reformed Church Poppin Centre tea room, I was developing a circle of acquaintances. I met other people who were retired, ill or needed companionship. I discovered that many coffee shops and cafes are like social services except that you couldn't tell the difference between the social workers and the clients!

One of these people I met, a lady about my age, happened also to suffer from C.F.S./M.E. Not only were these acquaintances becoming a new network of support for me, I realised that I was becoming the same for some of them. I understood that many people are glad of the chance to chat to someone. In fact telling your own story is probably quite therapeutic.

I did not have much energy but I did have time, a commodity often in short supply in a fast moving Western society. A very attractive businesswoman, whom I met in this fashion, was very supportive.

I did get confirmed into the church and with improving energy enjoyed going to services with my wife, without having to remain seated through-out the service as I had to do at one time. I always used the time to reflect on my situation and to be grateful for the good things in my life; like the growing recovery.

After each service with the coffee and socializing afterwards, which gave me another source of friends, I was always left with feelings of exhilaration and optimism.

My wife and I decided to go to some of the church social functions. We met other people who had suffered trials in their lives and were comforted by this. We were not the only ones.

In losing my job, I missed the association with colleagues; something I had not particularly valued until after I had retired and lost them. So it was pleasing to see my new social life gradually building, more varied and extensive than before. At this time though, nightmares were becoming more frequent. I would wake shouting and fighting as I repeatedly saw shadowy figures coming towards me out of the night. I dreamt I had died and these phantoms were coming for me. Another time I dreamt I had gone blind and sat up in bed in fear and dread repeating over and over again, "I'm blind, I'm blind". Then I thought to switch on the light and found I was alright.

Staying overnight at the house of some friends in the Lake District, I woke in the middle of the night to find myself stood in a dark room. Eventually I recollected in which house I was but I did not know where the bed was. I thought of shouting but dismissed this because of the ignominy I would suffer on being found. Putting on the light was the next thought; but where was the light switch? I began to get really worried. Then I noticed the faint light coming through the curtains. I recalled the plan of the room I had learnt in the daylight and worked out where the bed was in relation to the window and set off in that direction - feeling my way very gingerly. At last I found it and got back into bed.

At other times I have woken to find myself trying to leave the bedroom through the wardrobe door, giving away my whereabouts to my wife, who was woken up, with the rattling and scuffling.

The last incident involved suddenly leaping out of bed clutching the duvet and crashing into the opposite wall in an attempt to again fight off menacing figures approaching me, leaving my wife bereft in bed.

By now, I was discovering that not all of the consequences of having C.F.S./M.E. were bad. I have learnt about opera and wonder at the way Mozart in pieces like Cosi Fan Tutte speaks to us, of love, across the centuries. I have encountered the Christian faith and the value of a good marital relationship, strengthened by the reward of coping together with prolonged hardship. The pleasure in relaxation and a healthy attitude to managing myself, were other little gems of truth; and the power of psychology to explain and resolve personal distress is something I have enjoyed discovering. It is an Aladdin's cave overflowing with precious insights into the human condition. Through-out this period though, having rediscovered the enjoyment of living, I was anxious I would lose it all with one mistake and be setback, to the beginning all over again.

APRIL 1992.
At this time, I phoned my colleague to say I could now take on some private cases. However, the surprise was that my first case came from an independent primary school with whom I had worked when still with the local education authority.

The build up of anticipation, as the time to visit this case at his parent's home, was intense. I continually had to stop visions of not coping and replace them with fantasies of success.

I gained security from knowing I had coped well recently with all of the components of the work involved. I feared running out of energy before I had finished; of relapsing, but I had tested out these concerns weeks ago. There was nothing really to fear.
Knocking on the door of the detached house with a beautiful garden, a young woman let me in. I sat down in a pleasantly furnished lounge and over a cup of coffee she described the

worries she had had about her son. I began to relax. I could cope with analysing this mother's cares. Settling down at a table, putting the boy, aged ten, at his ease by talking about his family, had the same effect for me.

Half way through, I began to realise that I was feeling really well. I was working again.

Driving home I was ecstatic. I had done it. I felt larger than life, full of self-worth and confidence. I was coming back to what I knew best. The Department of Social Security call this, "therapeutic work" in cold official jargon, but I was amazed at just how powerful this therapy was. Sheer self-worth was probably the principal gain and the pleasure at having coped.

A cholestrol test was 6.9; a bit high.

SEPTEMBER 1992.
Now doing a private case at between once a fortnight to once a month, my spirit was growing stronger.

Becoming an invalid, losing your career status and feeling one's role as a father diminished, your esteem can fall, in the eyes of your children, who as a consequence can be tempted to treat you with growing contempt and disdain. This can generate negative moods. Having therapeutic work can help remedy this, as well as raising your own self-esteem.

In trying to cope with the hours of resting I still needed to do, I would enjoy thinking to myself. I had favourite thoughts that I liked to repeat; such as buying a new computer, what I would do in the coming days and weeks. However, as I did more and more of this, I gradually realised it was making me feel ill and the symptoms of headaches and hypoglycaemia that resulted, could last weeks.

The culprits were thoughts involving planning, solving problems using mental arithmetic, maths, the calendar or creating stories and thinking or speaking in a foreign language. It was the mental activity when lying down that was causing the problem, and not when using pencil and paper in desk-work. It was also quite difficult to suppress this type of analytical thinking. I enjoyed it.

Day-dreaming, in which I relaxed and allowed any thoughts and images to come and go, caused no problems and proved to be a pleasurable mind-game that I often played. It was interesting to just be like an observer in my head waiting and watching for whatever would come up next on my mental video display.

However, at first it was a chilling idea that I was so affected by C.F.S./M.E. that I could not allow myself the luxury even to think freely. To run one's life like this, with all of these physical and mental restrictions was awful. It took some time to get used to it.

As mentioned earlier, I first noticed the problem, when the mental activity in helping my elder daughter with her maths homework in the spring of 1989 caused a relapse and before that in August 1980 when I was working on solving statistics problems at work. My view is that every time a relapse is suffered the virus causing the illness escapes from infected muscle and brain cells where it lies dormant during a recovery period and again circulates in the bloodstream free to further infect other muscle and brain cells.

Between cases, I read alot and after one particular book, summarized its chapters and headings on to one sheet of A4 paper. Whilst lying down after lunch I decided to memorize this information and really enjoyed achieving this, until just over an hour later, I began to feel ill; horrible, with a characteristic headache. I guessed that in my enthusiasm I had spent too long exercising my brain. Avoiding all thinking or recalling of memories, it took several days for these symptoms and the hypoglycaemia that occurred, to fade. I realised that I must take greater care not to stress my brain too much and rationed myself to less than one hour a day of mental activity of this type. I decided that I just had to do what was necessary to stay well. However, many people with C.F.S./M.E. suffer from similar problems. Later I learnt meditation and found it very therapeutic along with thought-stopping; just deciding immediately to stop thinking of a thought or image.

Joining in the church barn dance was fun even though I only risked doing two dances, but it was good to watch and feel that I was taking part. I did have problems taking up a dancing position with one huge lady because every time I tried to dance with my arm around her waist, (what waist), I banged into her ample bust!

This, along with, visiting friends for the weekend and going on holiday were a tonic to my wife. We had feared that they might never be possible.

I recalled one of my saddest moments when, after a prolonged period of illness and the future looking bleak, my wife mooted the possibility of going on holiday abroad with the children without me. It was a logical suggestion given my circumstances. I am just relieved it never became necessary and notice that it has strengthened my determination to get well.

JANUARY 1993.
In January 1993, I had achieved two years without a relapse and I was succeeding in reducing the tranquillizer component (perphenazine) of the triptafen drug that I was taking. This coincided with a developing allergy to milk, cheese and yoghurt. My throat would swell up and become sore soon after eating any dairy produce. My subsequent reading about C.F.S./M.E. indicated that food allergies can be a common problem for sufferers.

Abandoning writing articles I embarked on writing this book. I visited the Barnes Medical Library of Birmingham University and with the help of a librarian using the computer medical database Medline, we searched 3,000 English language journals around the world and turned up 400 references on M.E. in half an hour. With careful editing, these were reduced to about 170 for which I collected a print out. This was to be a promising start.

However, work on my book was interrupted by the realisation of one of my greatest fears. My wife became very ill and with that, our roles were abruptly reversed. She became distressed by extreme abdominal pain. The G.P. advised admission to hospital and after waiting around in corridors and casualty cubicles, where I lay down on the floor to rest, she was eventually given a bed on a ward by 10-30 p.m. that night.

I drove home to explain all of this to my younger daughter. The elder one was living away from home sharing a student flat in Birmingham.

For years, ever since being first ill, I have agonized over the possibility of my wife dying and how I would cope. How would I cope with the bereavement and looking after myself and two daughters. This anxiety was controlled to a degree by having earlier formulated a contingency plan. I had listed all the information I would need to run the household.

My wife had not died fortunately, but I was now going to have to juggle running the household with avoiding relapsing. How would I do it? I was now able to do three and a half hours of **physical** activity when spaced out over the day.

I slept well that night through sheer fatigue but in the early hours of the morning, my worries began to ferment like yeast in a beer vat. I gave up trying to sleep and got dressed. It was time to take a look at my contingency plan.

As I worked through the day using the washing machine, dishwasher and microwave all my notes on how to operate them were perfect.

This learning progressed well and with it my confidence. A weekly schedule of household events like washing, shopping, putting out the bin etc. recipes and cooking instructions were in my contingency plan and all helped.

All writing and private cases stopped. I, in no way had the energy to do both roles. I worked on household activities alternating with rest. When resting I used all of the anxiety-reducing techniques I had learnt from earlier times. My younger daughter, now in the lower sixth form at school became a good team mate as we jointly worked on the daily chores.

I managed, with my wife's help to put the supermarket shopping list in the right order for going round the store with the minimum of effort. (For subsequent weeks I ran the list off on the computer). Even so, it took two hours to get the fortnightly shopping done with a break after an hour for a cup of tea in the cafeteria. It was surprising how physically taxing some jobs were, like hanging out heavy washing on the line, taking a quarter of an hour of lifting.

Each day brought new tasks and offers of help from family and neighbours. My brother mowed the lawns and a neighbour did some ironing.

My parents invited my younger daughter and myself for meals and a number of friends telephoned. But even this well-meant concern was a strain. The talking took time and energy and in the end I took the phone off the hook.

I got through to the weekend and managed to cook the chicken for the Sunday dinner. But I did make some mistakes. My daughter asked why she had only one leaf of cabbage. I agreed that it did look meagre, but I had only cooked one leaf each. I had miscalculated because the cooking had reduced the cabbage to a limp flat offering.

I had wondered what to do with all the cabbage that was left! As it turned out, I practised cooking it in the evening and we had it for supper; a plateful each! Well, it was fun; we had a joke about it. You cannot get to be Cordon Bleu standard all in a week.

In fact I was developing a sneaking admiration for my wife's culinary skills. It was not easy to end up with all of the food cooked and ready to serve at the same time.

Keeping up with daily visits to the hospital was tiring. It took ten minutes to walk from the car park to the ward and once there I was cast in the opposite role. I was a carer now. I had to listen to my wife's concerns about sleeping badly because there was always someone being ill in the ward at night. Her temperature was not coming down even on antibiotics. She might need an operation but the doctor was vacillating. If it was an abscess on the appendix as he suspected, it could be left, as many cleared up without surgery.

My wife (Susan) was feeling exhausted. She felt she would get more rest at home and a few days later, on condition that she promised that she would stay in bed until her temperature was normal, she was discharged.

After three weeks in our new roles we were both becoming aware of what the other had had to cope with. Susan found out how hard it was to feel equable when confined and allowed to do next to nothing for weeks. (I had done it for years). But I found out just how much mental effort went into running a household. It is like running your own business. Any successful housewife who says she is trained for nothing, is under-estimating herself.

However I was enjoying the control and power to make decisions. I had developed a routine which I found involved less thinking. Also I rested in the week in order to have more energy at the weekends, when more demands were made; shopping, Sunday dinner, hospital visits etc.

When Susan was declared well again and given permission to leave her bed, she had a long convalescence to endure. She agreed to pace herself; to increase her physical activity very gradually and to avoid dysfunctional beliefs like: "I'll never get back to my job".

She controlled anxiety with relaxation and increased her confidence with positive thinking. All the knowledge I had learnt from being ill was now coming in useful. I realised it could be applicable to any major illness. I thought again that this must belong to a psychology of illness.

Not only did I try to apply this knowledge, but I tried to emulate the role-model of a good carer that Susan had provided in looking after me. I endeavoured to be there for her when she needed me; being supportive but not negative, not reprimanding or critical and avoiding giving too much advice when it was not asked for. We carefully analysed problems that occurred and were pleased with progress and coping. I tried to ignore and not over-react to any irritability and tetchiness due to her illness.

As she improved she was keen to take back the roles and tasks she had given up and I graciously gave them back. However, I resolved not to forget what I had learnt and to avoid as far as possible the sick-role that many invalids can easily allow themselves to unnecessarily occupy. Susan was helpful in this. It can be a problem for some, since the improvement in the sufferer and their increasing independence diminishes the role of the carer. Some carers cannot accept this. Having a contingency plan had been wise. It had worked excellently.

I began to realise that not only do you need medical advice when ill, but also psychological information to help both the invalid and carer to cope better. This could become a major growth area for clinical psychology in medical general practice and hospitals in the future both in preventive healthcare and in the amelioration of the iatrogenic effects of medical treatment. The self-management of the recently discovered psychological factors contributing to many illnesses, previously thought of as purely medical, is another potential growth area.

Once everything was back to normal, I felt a great deal of satisfaction that I had, with the limitations of C.F.S./M.E., managed to run the household for a month.

SEPTEMBER 1993.
For the year from September 1993 to September 1994 I continued to see private cases and write this book. Since first becoming ill in 1979 - I had probably one bout of flu and a couple of colds in 14 years. This was much fewer than prior to 1979. I feel sure my immune system is up-regulated, possibly due to the effects of C.F.S./M.E. or the anti-depressant drug amitriptyline.

A principal aim has been to try to reduce the tranquilliser component, perphenazine, of my triptafen medication. Many symptoms like, difficulties going to sleep, dry chest feeling, constipation, dry nose, fatigue, aches and pains and recurrent hypoglycaemia all made the reduction very problematic and slow.

I endeavoured to reduce the drug with the minimum of withdrawal effects, by doing it as gradually as possible so that I could continue to work and enjoy life. One pleasant surprise was that feelings of pleasure were much more heightened after reducing the drug. I think tranquillizers do truncate negative feelings but also the positive ones as well.

The next major problem would be trying to reduce the anti-depressant amitriptyline without precipitating recurrent relapsing as happened in September 1988.

I live in the hope that my health will continue to be maintained and improve.

As I have progressed I have tried to reinstate the skills I had before I was ill. Besides travelling to different places seeing children and students referred to me, in 1995 I was invited to give some lectures. I was pleased with these requests but aware that I needed to relearn how to cope with such situations. So I needed to do a speech that was not too demanding. I decided to give one at my 25th wedding anniversary.

I rested all day so that I would have the energy to cope with the evening. The speech, the story of my married life over the last 25 years, was a chronological list of funny stories which were easy to remember. I listed the key word for each, on a small card as an aide memoire. Mental rehearsal of my speech and the avoidance of fantasies of failure engendered confidence. I decided to only do the speech if I felt I had the energy to do it without pushing myself.

As it turned out, I did do it, and it was a success. I am really proud of myself for having achieved it. I am now looking forward to my next speech.

I was now working for some of the time, as efficiently as I could seeing private cases and writing, to try to assuage the guilt of failing to maintain a full-time job and a good income for my family. It dispels the accusation of some, that I do not work.

JANUARY 1995.
At this point in time, I was able to be up and about for 11 hours, sleep for 10 and a half hours and had to lie down in the daytime

for two and a half hours each day. It had been 3 years 360 days since the last relapse in January 1991.

I was able to do physical activity in short spells for a total of 4 hours per day and writing, reading or computing for 7 hours per day; total activity did not exceed 7 hours. However these levels of activity could not be maintained every day when I was reducing the medication. The greatest risk of a relapse, comes if you try to change your routine or your medication.

Sometimes there was a bad day whilst reducing the perphenazine when I was reminded of the periods of lying down for three or four hours and becoming exhausted again after 5 minutes sitting up; of the dilemma of being bored with passivity - but too tired to do anything and being like this for month after month. There is value in remembering these bad times because they remind you of what you have now and where you have come from.

By this time I was enjoying life, but care was needed not to appear to be enjoying it too much, as some working people seem to think that if you are chronically ill you should be miserable. Some have actually envied my circumstances. My reply to them, was "work part-time, half your income like I had to, and you can do the same".

In September 1995 I started taking salt with my food again after finding that I had very low blood pressure. I had stopped taking it some years before on health grounds, but subsequently found out that people with low blood pressure should not desist from taking it.

By February 2001 I had continued to maintain this level of health and periodically reduce the dosage of amitriptyline and perphenazine but with great difficulty. Each very small reduction took months from which to recover.

I am still surprised by events that drain me of energy and set me back sometimes weeks, though never a full relapse. Seeing a sad film easily depresses me. Standing still for twenty minutes to half an hour; getting cold; doing anaerobic chores or DIY jobs for more than 20 minutes to half an hour or going out for the evening are all examples of occasions that have caused setbacks.

COPING STRATEGIES.

Whenever I meet a new sufferer with C.F.S./M.E., I always suggest that it is a great mistake to try to struggle on with their job or old lifestyle. As soon as the illness has been diagnosed you should organise your life so that you never get tired. As soon as you feel the slightest weariness stop and rest until you feel completely well again.

Do not give up hope. Many sufferers do recover somewhat with rest and time. When well I very gradually tried to rebuild my life and relearn old skills.

I have kept a detailed diary of my activities and health. For example;

Day 1 (after a relapse) Sunday 17th April 1988.
07-00 am. Slight anxiety. Relaxation stopped it.
10-03 am. Sat up, breakfast.
10-18 am. " " 15 minutes, feeling excellent.
10-40 am. Listening to the radio.
11-00 am. " " tired now.
etc.

*

Later I amended the diary format to;
3yrs 354days (after a relapse) Mon 2nd Jan 1995.
8-30 Got up till lunch 1pm.   up 4.5hrs
P (4-00 hrs) 15 min walk+ 15 min bath
P+W+R (7-00 hrs) 15 min walk+ 15 min bath +60 min writing
Thinking (2 hours)
Reminders.
Don't read lying down.

Don't talk too much.
Relax - clear mind.
O.K.   Total. Up and about 4.5 hours.

Key: P   = total amount of physical activity allowed in a day.
P+W+R = total amount of physical,writing and reading allowed
           in a day.
Thinking; amount allowed per day.

This lay-out on each page of a notebook provides a reminder everyday of what I am allowed to do and a running total of what I have done. At the end of the day I record O.K. if I have felt well all day. This record is then summarized onto graph paper, so that a month's information can be viewed at once.

This gave a record of how well I had been, which sustained me through periods of illness. Often in the middle of such a period you forget how well you have been in the past. Realising this, means you can look forward to the return of better health, with rest and time with renewed hope.

I tried to eliminate the cycle of good and bad days which makes your health and energy unpredictable. Such variation makes planning ahead for any social life and voluntary or part-time work for either the carer or sufferer, impossible. This can be a strain on the relationship between partners.

Therefore, an absolute first priority is to get onto an even keel. No matter how ill you are, you must note down how much you can do of walking, reading or writing etc. **without any difficulty whatsoever** in a sustainable way each day. At first I could only sit up in a chair for five minutes per day. This was therefore where I started. I did this once an hour until it was so easily achieved that I was able to contemplate increasing it by a minute. At the same time I changed nothing else. I did this repeatedly until I could do half an hour. At that point I was well enough to see visitors for strictly this amount of time in my bedroom.

In this way I built up walking to an hour and a half, and reading and writing to seven hours a day interspersed with rest. Always the increment added after each improvement was very small. I measured everything in minutes.

However, I have had to avoid all housework and gardening; in fact anything remotely energetic. In September 1994 I pruned some trees for a quarter of an hour. Heavy fatigue followed and lasted for five hours. **I don't do it any more.**

Later however, I eventually have mowed the lawn with a light electric mower for quarter of an hour and on another occasion hung out washing for a quarter of an hour doing each once in the day and been O.K.

CONCLUSION.
I put my partial recovery down to the Efamol, Magnesium injections, amitriptyline anti-depressant, taking salt again with my food to counter low blood pressure, plenty of filtered drinking water, a balanced diet high in fruit and vegetables, a gluten-free and dairy-free diet, gradually increasing amounts of walking, some purposeful activity everyday, the love and support of my wife and family, having a Christian faith, going to church and church social events and above all else - careful self-management.

Sometimes I can easily delude myself into thinking that I am cured. I look well. Most of the time I do not feel any fatigue but I know from past experience that it would be folly not to rest at the appropriate times. The better I feel, the more I am tempted to do too much. However, I rarely succumb because of what my experience of C.F.S./M.E. has taught me. With this illness I have found that the fatigue comes hours or days after the initial exertion.

Continually, I emphasize to my daughters the merits of taking care of themselves, not punishing but rewarding themselves and working in a **sustainable** enjoyable manner. Developing C.F.S./M.E. or other stress-related illness is a risk if they do not.

I wish I had taken more notice of the augurs I undoubtedly experienced. I had absolutely no knowledge of chronic illness amongst adults or that the pain and anguish I have suffered existed. I had only seen it in sick children at special schools. I had no expectation that it could happen to me. When I worked excessively hard, I enjoyed it in a masochistic sort of way and had no idea of the personal risks I was running.

In hindsight I would have been less altruistic and more circumspect about excessive attempts at self-enhancement.

I was addicted to the pleasure I derived from my career. In retrospect I would be much more careful with my health, (or at least I like to think I would) in the same way that married people would be much less inclined to have extra-marital affairs, if they were fully aware of the risks that were possible, such as the lasting financial and psychological damage to themselves, their partner and their children.

However, I shall always be grateful for the improvement in my health and quality of life. I am at pains to avoid being greedy in my quest to restore my family's fortunes. The way I live must be enjoyably **sustainable**.

I am pleased that I decided to undertake the very difficult task of reducing the dosage of the tranquillizer, perphenazine. My feelings of pleasure are much more frequent and much sharper than the rather dull, flat feelings I had before. G.P.s rarely if ever help patients devise detailed medication reduction programmes.

In evaluating your life it is often difficult to see any causative pattern until many years can be scanned at a time. I have had a problem with over-motivation; setting standards for my work, too high to be sustainable over the years. This trait may have been learnt in my upbringing at home and at school, with the desire to please authority and to keep striving until it was achieved. Strangely, I am now more happy than I have ever been. I do not take anything for granted any more; I value everything and look for sustainable enjoyment in all I do.

Since my illness, I have only once been described as a failure. My reaction was that I have so far survived C.F.S./M.E., no mean feat in itself. That a successful life is more important than a successful career and that life is not yet over, is self evident! I am aware that, though harrowing for my family and me, there are people who are much more gravely debilitated by C.F.S./M.E. than myself; some confined to bed or their bedroom. These people need to be part of a home-visiting service, that provides them with a social support network of their own. This might be provided by other more fortunate members of a local C.F.S./M.E. support group or even via a computer, webcam and the internet.

My philosophy of life which I feel sure contributed to the onset of C.F.S./M.E. has changed and now consists of Christian principles, plus the avoidance of personal stress, A type behaviour (rushing about) that is a causal factor in heart disease and type C behaviour (not expressing one's real feelings) which is associated with cancer. I now try to look for enjoyment in every little activity.

Although I would not recommend it, having C.F.S./M.E. has doubled my life experience. Maybe learning from it, ensures that not all of the effects of illness are necessarily detrimental.

As a direct consequence of having to retire from my career, but then having the opportunity to write this book about C.F.S./M.E. I have read more about the psychology of illness in the last few years than ever before. It has been like being on a personally designed college course. I have been reminded of the value of my relationships with my family and friends and the need to actively give time to maintaining them. Without C.F.S./M.E. I might have lived life without realising their true value; to have taken them for granted; to have missed their significance. So often people only realise the worth of what they have when they lose it.

It is now April 2008. In recent years my health has continued to improve slowly, but I still rest every hour for 15 minutes during the day; rest for an hour at lunchtime and teatime; walk for 45 minutes morning and afternoon; am awake for 15 hours a day and sleep about 9 hours; take the multivitamin supplement Multibionta 50+; still have a gluten-free and dairy-free diet, take the supplement Lecithin which the body uses to rebuild cell walls; and am gradually reducing the dose of amitriptyline. It is the latter three measures that seem to have brought recent improvement. I work part-time for myself. Continuing part-time work has allowed my to come off Incapacity Benefit and to feel the consequent increase in self-esteem. However, I see one case a week on one day and type up the report the next day.

The daily diary of my activity helps me keep a tight control on my self-management; avoiding doing too much or too little each day. It is my Bible; through its use I can see the effect of changes in treatments and activity.

PART 1 REFERENCES
Behan, P.O. & Bakheit, A.M.O. (1991). Clinical spectrum of post-viral fatigue syndrome. British Medical Bulletin, 47, 4, 793-808.

Cooper, C. L. (1981). The Stress Check. Coping with the Stresses of Life and Work. Englewood Cliffs, N.J.07632: Prentice-Hall, Inc., Spectrum Books.

***

PART 2. SPIRITUAL ASPECTS OF C.F.S./M.E.

CHAPTER 1. PHILOSOPHY OF LIFE.

In April 2003 a search of the world wide web (www) for websites about Chronic Fatigue Syndrome was completed using the search engine www.google.co.uk. Only 4 websites in the world and none in the U.K. provide information about C.F.S./M.E. with a Christian philosophy.

The **beliefs** of sufferers can greatly influence the course of their C.F.S./M.E. Books that explore the connection between religious beliefs and C.F.S./M.E. are Midgley, (2000) and Rotholz, (2002).

The beliefs you hold are part of a philosophy of life. The beliefs of a patient can aid or hinder their healing and recovery. This is apparent in experimental trials of new drugs in which a random allocation of patients to an experimental group (who receive the new drug) and a control group (who believe they are receiving the drug but in fact receive a placebo such as a harmless sugar tablet) are compared. Often the placebo group recover nearly as well as those in the experimental group receiving the new drug. This is called the placebo effect.

The placebo group do so well, because these patients believe they are getting the effective new drug. Therefore beliefs can greatly aid recovery from illness and should be part of the treatment process. Some doctors are already noticing that a medicine that has no biological action can heal through the placebo effect, because the patient **believes** it is helping them.

I would predict that a development in medical treatment regimes in the future, will include a focus on people's beliefs – i.e. their spirituality.

Suffering from this illness has not just affected me physically and mentally but also spiritually. In the same way as every experience we have, shapes all of us and our lives, so too C.F.S./M.E. has changed my whole outlook or philosophy of life.

Philosophy refers to the study of origins and principles, of causes and reasons with practical wisdom and calmness of temper. I want to discuss here the way this illness has altered my thinking and perceptions.

Cohen (1976) describes a number of scales for evaluating the values held by people.

In May 1994 the fourth edition of the Diagnostic and Statistical Manual of Mental Disorders (commonly called DSM-IV) was published. This is where newly defined maladies can be found and relevant here is one called **spiritual disorder**.

This category is used in the event of distressing experiences that involve spiritual values occurring. It takes into account near-death, transcendental or religious experiences and a host of other events which **precipitate an upsetting change of values**. It is exactly this latter situation that can be caused by the onset of a chronic illness like C.F.S./M.E.

For someone undergoing such a re-adjustment of identity with all of its painful wrenches and upheaval, an allied and non-intrusive listener might be more helpful than a psychiatrist with a label for a new mental disorder. However, the advent of this new category provides a focus for such phenomenon, allowing people's experiences to be collected and analysed.

For me, my philosophy of life just before the onset of C.F.S./M.E. I think was partly instrumental in precipitating my illness, as said earlier, but the major re-orientation in values forced on me by this experience has I think been one of the factors contributing to my recovery. Erquhart Tolle the author of the best selling book "The

Power of Now" published in 2001 by Hodder Mobius, is all about spirituality and enlightenment, and he recognises this phenomenon. The book is very powerful and a summary is included below:

The author is German with a degree from London University. Some time was spent lecturing at Cambridge University. He says "You are here to enable the divine purpose of the universe to unfold. That is how important you are".

The preface indicates that this book is about a shift in consciousness and spiritual enlightenment. He says that the planet needs a change in human consciousness to survive. There is a search for how to remain in a peak experience state always.

Man can develop further spiritually; we are all connected with each other, the environment and the cosmos. There is more than just the physical reality. See David Bohm's multidimensional model of reality. The soul (true self) lies behind our body, emotions and a chattering mind. Our ultimate destiny is to reconnect to the soul.

The author describes how he had depression and anxiety until he was aged 30. He thought 'I hate myself' and felt that there were two parts to himself. He asked himself which was real; the 'I' or the self. The 'I' rejected the self after intense depression. He felt born again and that light is love. The self collapsed. The 'I' felt at peace now and saw the beauty of nature.

He realised that his mind had caused his problems. With this enlightenment he became a spiritual teacher, lecturing groups of people all over the world.

He said that you must identify what is false in your mind. The real 'I' involves the joy of Being plus inner peace. Enlightenment is feeling connected to something greater, along with a peace that is an escape from incessant thinking.

He continues saying that Being, is in our life and in all life. In you it is the true self accessed by meditation, and concentrating on the Now, so as to stop the mental chatter. Thinking is a barrier separating one from God, from others and from bliss. You are not your mind, therefore switch off thinking to produce silence. You can observe your own mind from a higher level. The mind worries, generating a voice in the head which can result in mental illness. The mind can be a tormentor.

Free yourself from your mind. Concentrating on Now only – stops the thinking chatter through meditation. (I would say that keeping busy in bereavement to mask one's troubled thoughts may exhaust you. The answer may be to try to learn to switch off the thoughts to bring silence and relief.)

Compulsive thinking is an addiction. Ego is the false self.

Mind is a stage in the evolution of consciousness. Meditation; mental stillness allows connection to the universal consciousness. Some call this 'God'.

Creativity, new ideas etc. come from meditation and mental silence. Emotions are the body's reactions to the state of mind. Your emotion tells you what your mind is really thinking.

Observe your emotions as well as your thoughts. Negative emotions are like pain. Positive emotions i.e. love come from being connected with the Being (God). Peace, love and joy come in meditation i.e. mental stillness. Emotion oscillates from pleasure to pain.

All cravings and addictions are a substitute for the joy of Being – (in the present and connected to God). Emotional pain comes for the same reason and causes physical pain and disease.

Most pain is unnecessary. It comes from the non-acceptance of what 'is'. To stop making pain, live more in the Now, i.e. this moment. Past and future are for running your life, but only use them when necessary. Accept pain – work with it and don't fight against it.

Accumulated pain (pain body) from the past can persist and generate a negative outlook which rejects joy. The pain body can lead to illness and suicide. Expose pain to the light of the Now. Focus on the pain. Watching or observing the pain means you accept it for what it is now and it will heal. (I would suggest that this could be tested experimentally).

A spiritual teacher helps others watch their mind, emotions and pain – helping their perceptions become light that transforms the pain into healing. The mind is the ego and it acts to protect itself.

Being the observer of the mind/ego stops the fear of the ego being humiliated, stops your ego defending itself all the time- i.e. in fear all the time – as most people are. (Therefore I would suggest, when meeting **new** people, don't give them cause to fear you). The mind creates a false self – the ego - as a substitute for your true self rooted in Being (God). The ego strives for completeness with external trappings of success.

Tolle says "You are a branch cut off from the vine" , as Jesus put it. Enjoy Now, the present – don't live for the past or the future. This is the key to spiritual enlightenment.

A Sufi Muslim, a great poet and teacher said "Past and future veil God from our sight" Take every opportunity to step out of the past and the future – and fully focus on the present, i.e. now. When threatened, focus on the present to avoid the egoic response.

Past, future, the mind, planning, and predicting are all necessary but not all the time. **Use the present moments to observe the way on the journey of life; enjoy it.**

Psychological time is time spent agonizing over the past or, for example, living by a rigid belief system that generates – hell for people now – for the promise of a so-called better future. i.e. communism, extremism etc. The present can be bad, but not in the Now. You cannot be unhappy in the Now. There are no problems in the Now only situations that can be dealt with now or left alone and accepted. Problems create pain. In a life or death situation you are totally in the present – survive or die. It is not a problem.

He exhorts you to ask yourself if there is joy in what you are doing. If it is all struggle then psychological time has taken you over, covering the present moment. Having too much to do can do this. Decide what to do then just enjoy it with full attention on the present now in doing it and the fruit of your action will come of itself; and feel peace and love. Everything is honoured; but nothing matters.

Deep suffering often leads to transformation to the Now – realising the present. (Are children more in the present – now, than adults?) Ordinary unconsciousness (OU) occurs when the normal egoic mind is in control and is occupied by work, TV, etc., and this state is varied with short term pleasures, like alcohol, drugs, sex etc..

Unhappiness is deep unconsciousness (DU) and can result in violence. In OU resistance to what 'is' creates discontent. When stressed most people go from OU to DU but a conscious person – i.e. able to become present – and is able to witness their own mind, when stressed, will do more consciousness. (Someone who is bereaved can be tempted to keep busy in order to mask the pain of grief, but perhaps, judging from Erquart Tolle, they should learn to meditate and silence they mind to find peace and love.)

Western civilisation has been imbued with ordinary unconsciousness since before Christ, in its population and it is paralleled by a loss of connection with Being (God). It is due to the loss of presence; always wanting and craving something. In order to leave OU, ask yourself what you are thinking; ask how you feel. Monitor yourself. What is causing these negative thoughts or emotions? These cause unhappiness. Work to resolve these issues, says Tolle.

Complaining is non-acceptance of what 'is'. Speaking out is empowering; change it or leave it or accept it. Where ever you are, be there totally.

Waiting for something to happen – means you are waiting for the future, not living in the present. Be grateful for what you have now. That is prosperity. Enjoy the present always. There is outer purpose – ambition; and inner purpose which is enlightenment.

Attend to your behaviour, emotions, desires and thoughts as they all affect behaviour and thinking as they are in the present.

To enter the state of presence close your eyes and watch for the next thought. You wait a long time because intense presence is free of thought; the mind is still. Meditate. Being body-aware and listening to your body keeps you 'presented'; so does the beauty of nature. (I have become aware of the beauty of other people, men, women and children. They are equally part of nature). All things have a 'consciousness' to some extent. The watcher or witness is pure consciousness beyond form; i.e. enlightenment.

Tolle quotes Jesus's parables in support of Jesus's acceptance of 'presence'.

He continues saying that the egoic mind is unconscious; there are now egoic countries. Alcohol, drugs, addictions etc. give a partial relief from the egoic mind.

You can substitute 'Christ' ' for 'presence'. Those with presence can recognize others with it. Presence shines with a light. People with presence, meeting together produce a presence and light. It frees you from the illusion of only living in mind and body. You are alive in consciousness.

'Unconsciousness' is a word for 'sin' and 'insanity' explains Tolle. Countries need to become 'present' to get connected to the Being (God) and to love to live in a different way from the egoic mind. Learn self-awareness of the inner body and mind. Denying the body, sex or association, like nuns, monks, ascetics etc. does not lead to enlightenment..

Enlightenment comes through self-awareness of the body; acceptance of it; don't fight against the body. Be self-aware of the inner body all the time to be connected to God. It is 'presence' in the 'Now'. Do it in traffic jams to enjoy.

When a crisis arises, look at your inner body; be self-aware – an answer will form.

Forgiveness is important.

Inner or self-awareness slows down the aging process, improves the immune system and self-healing. Morning and night, meditate and focus on each organ of the body with consciousness. Being creative or problem-solving improves when you meditate for a few minutes between thinking.

When listening to others, be self-aware; don't be thinking your own thoughts. Relationships are spoilt by not listening.

Meditation links us to the Being (God). Be self-aware (in presence) all the time in daily life. Being in presence allows the love of the Being (God) to enter you. **The universe is the 'body' of God and when 'present' we are all part of it.**

Tolle reminds us, **"You are here to enable the divine purpose of the universe to unfold. That is how important you are".**

If you miss all the opportunities for spiritual realization in your life, a portal opens when you die and through ignorance many misunderstand this portal of light and turn away in fear. Western culture teaches nothing of this knowledge of death.

Salvation is here and now. It is understanding that you are part of God. Presence helps make all your relationships loving. (Lust, greed, envy etc. are the ego at work).

Acceptance of what 'is' frees you from mind and makes presence possible. i.e. accept completely your partner as they are, to achieve a long loving relationship.

Love is a state of Being. In the stillness of presence you can feel the love of God within you. When another person feels this at the same time – then you are both truly communicating, not one egoic mind relating to another.

Marital crises are an opportunity to become conscious and presented and accepting - not judgemental of your partner. Too many people are looking for this enlightenment in falling in love with others and being disappointed. In a crisis, be the observer, the watcher; step back from inside the situation and your egoic mind. Your partner is likely to become conscious; 'presented'. Express yourself without blaming your partner. Listen to him/her.

Enlightenment involves love and joy, openness and presence with all people. A crisis is an opportunity for presence (not the egoic mind) to solve the crisis by inviting the partner to be 'presented'. (As I write these notes the portent of the words is inspiring, ennervating and satisfying. Typing up these notes is like re-reading the book and revisiting the pleasure.)

Tolle thinks that **women are closer to enlightenment than men. Early man saw God as female. Only when the mind came more to the fore, was God seen as male and females were subordinated.**

Connection to God requires surrender, non-judgement, openness, allowing life to be, instead of resisting it; these are more feminine traits. The obstacle to enlightenment for men is the **mind** and for women – **the pain-body** he says.

The pain-body is the sum total of pain experienced by a person or a society (country). It can lead to being a perpetrator or victim of violence or to enlightenment. The number of enlightened women out numbers men. The pain-body can free you from the identification with mind and therefore lead to enlightenment.

Being emotionally attached or identified with the pain prevents enlightenment. Be the watcher and the attachment is broken. Victims blame their state on the criminal but the victim has the power of the present moment, to break from the past and start anew. Collective victim identity is when women say 'look what men did to women'.

Tolle suggests that **men have abused women over the millennia** but women today should not derive a sense of self from it and imprison themselves in the collective victim identity. If a woman is holding on to this anger etc. she is holding on to her pain-body. This blocks development of enlightenment and builds ego that does the same thing.

Any pain or emotion that you like, your presence transmutes it. Don't let pain take over your thinking. Be self-aware of all your emotions, body symptoms and sensations and observe, watch; stand back from them and accept.

This acceptance transmutes the pain-body into radiant consciousness. Do this every time you have pain – for women do it at menstruation. Presence regains consciousness from the mind. When your wife is troubled by the pain-body and is irritable, it is not her speaking but her mind. If the partner is in 'presence' he can see it is not her real self or consciousness. It is her egoic mind responding to the pain. Therefore he should not retaliate with defensive comments but help her into presence.

Even being enlightened and with peace of mind, you still need a relationship with the opposite sex if you have that need. But being enlightened helps you relate deeply, i.e. enlightened – conscious of Being or God.

Unhappiness says Tolle, can be a great awakener to presence. The solution is to accept this moment fully. You do need to love and accept yourself. In enlightenment 'you' and 'yourself ' are one. So then there is no need to love yourself- you are one.

When you live in complete acceptance of what is the best way to live, there is no good or bad. There is only higher good which includes the bad. Acceptance frees you from the dominance of your mind and re-connects you to God, and His consciousness will flow into your activity. In your presence you can feel the love of God and will love all creation. There is a field of consciousness around you – healing those in the field – by holding the frequency of intense presence. The ego acts to combat fear and lack, but it can lead to greed, power-seeking, control etc. causing conflict and illness.

Collective ego is the cause of wars. There is no ego when 'presented', no argument but complete acceptance of what is; no conflict within or between people.

Failure and suffering often lead to a search for spirituality. Getting self-worth from achieving completion of jobs is an identification with external factors; identification with mind. To an extreme this compulsion leads the body to become ill to force a stop. Being presented solves this. The advertising industry would collapse if people became enlightened and no longer sought to find their identity through buying things.

Negativism strengthens the ego. Presence stops it. (I have often found that when I am swearing to myself negativism is occurring). Use this as a trigger for 'presence'. e.g. a car alarm goes off and stimulates irritation in you. The irritation does not solve anything. Let it pass through you. Try to stop the alarm o.k. but don't over react.

Don't be dependent on the outer world for fulfillment or happiness – Tolle tells us to get it from presence. Every moment is the best moment now. At the level of Being (God) all suffering is seen as an illusion.

Being or consciousness, in others can be triggered and appear as healing. Compassion is the realization of the deep bond between yourself, all people and creation. St. Paul says the whole of creation is waiting for humans to become enlightened.

Enjoy the world, and make it part of yourself but don't get attached to it.

Once enlightened, he says, **others may notice the peace that emanates from you. You teach through Being, demonstrating the peace of God. You become the 'light of the world' emanating pure consciousness, eliminating unconsciousness in the world; making it a better world. Let your peace flow into whatever you do.**

In a problem, surrender to the circumstances; go with the flow, accept this moment and through reconnection to Being (God) you will be energized to find a solution without the egoic mind. More people on Earth need to have presence to use spiritual energy – the light from God – for us to move to a fairer world.

When ill, go with how you feel. Accept it; gain presence and enlightenment and God's love. Don't blame yourself or anything else for the illness.

Some people become conscious after a bereavement, deep suffering, pain or other disasterous events. They surrender to the situation and accept, are presented, entering a state of grace, enlightenment and feel the love of God. It is like crucifixion, resurrection and ascension.

With physical pain, face it; concentrate your attention on it. Full attention is full acceptance and the power of your presence removes time. Without time there is no suffering; no negativity can survive.

God is not separate from us. God is Being, not a being. Our being is God. Tolle recognises that most people only awaken through **suffering** to enlightenment. People who are unconscious and driven by their mind and its learned patterns of behaviour and conditioning, experience limited choice. Presence brings consciousness and real choice.

* * *

The following principles and quotations may aid the coping with chronic illness. They have given me a sharp sense of delight as each new concept has dawned on me. It was like eureka; I understand. At the very depths of my despair, I kept a copy of them beside me throughout the day. They were a lifeline of divine support. They made the difference and kept hope alive until better days were in sight. I knew many of the quotations by heart and as the darkness encroached, I would recite them aloud to myself to find relief.

I doubt that many of these thoughts are original but they are an indication of what can be learnt from an illness experience. It is another dimension and is to be contrasted with the reader's own philosophy of life, knowledge and experience.

Your philosophy of life drives the way you behave. Even a total lack of philosophy will have a bearing on your thinking and behaviour.

These realisations have been slowly distilled from over 28 years of experience of this illness and are important in that reading them may help cut short the long and harrowing path of discovery for other chronically ill people.

Having a philosophy of life is not an optional add-on but an indispensable guide in a confusing world. The greatest sources available to develop this philosophy are the Christian religion, other religions, and the history of human experience. Anyone without these is like a piece of flotsam adrift in the sea.

The Christian faith is a ready-made philosophy of life, that has been tried and tested over thousands of years.

Man requires to live by a philosopy of life; if he does not learn a beneficent one, a malevalent one can take root.

We must live life in the light of the experiences of the generations who have gone before. One can learn from their mistakes and prosper from their wisdom.

One can maximize the likelihood of good fortune by heeding the rules that past generations have discovered aid well-being and decrease the chance malevalence. The Ten Commandments are one such set of rules.

DESIDERATA.
Go placidly amid the noise and haste and remember what peace there may be in silence. As far as possible, without surrender, be on good terms with all persons. Speak your truth quietly and clearly and listen to others, even the dull and ignorant; they too have their story.

Avoid loud and aggressive persons, they are vexacious to the spirit. If you compare yourself with others, you may become vain or bitter; for always there will be greater and lesser persons than yourself. Enjoy your achievements as well as your plans.

Keep interested in your own career. However humble: it is a real possession in the changing fortunes of time.

Exercise caution in your business affairs; for the world is full of trickery. But let this not blind you to what virtue there is: many persons strive for high ideals; and everywhere life is full of heroism.

Be yourself. Especially do not feign affection. Neither be cynical about love; for in the face of all aridity and disenchantment it is as perennial as the grass.

Take kindly the counsel of the years, gracefully surrendering the things of youth. Nurture strength of spirit to shield you in sudden misfortune. But do not distress yourself with imaginings. Many fears are born of fatigue and loneliness. Beyond a wholesome discipline, be gentle with yourself. You are a child of the universe, no less than the trees and the stars: you have a right to be here. And whether or not it is clear to you, no doubt the universe is unfolding as it should.

Therefore be at peace with God, whatever you conceive Him to be and whatever your labours and aspirations; in the noisy confusion of life keep peace with your soul. With all its sham, drudgery and broken dreams, it is still a beautiful world. Be careful. Strive to be happy. Author unknown.

This Desiderata in fact encapsulates a philosophy of life. So too does the passage below.

Be merry all your life,
Toil no more than is required,
Nor cut short the time allotted to pleasure,
Don't waste time on daily cares
Beyond providing for your household,
And when wealth has come, follow your heart.

Wealth does no good if you are glum.
Author unknown.
Written in Egypt 3,500 years ago.

Maybe one can infer someone's philosophy of life from their behaviour.

The trouble with working out your own philosophy of life, is you don't know where each behaviour you take up may lead, or what it may lead to; e.g. drug-taking, crime etc.

Traditional religion often involves a tried and tested way of life.

In the West, pursuit of material things is the main preoccupation, but more fulfilling is a pursuit of knowledge and spiritual development.

FALSE GODS.

There are dangers in building a philosophy of life on solely money, power, food, drink, social and intellectual status, promotion at work, fashion, going out socially, expensive houses etc. None of these things are necessarily wrong in themselves but it is possible to be so obsessed with earning more money in business or getting promoted in one`s career that they exclude all else.

We all know of people consumed with owning a huge house and sacrificing all to that end. There are people who buy clothes far beyond their needs rarely wearing most of them just to be in the fashion.

There are others who live for going out to night-clubs socializing and drinking and leaving room for little else. It is a special sort of greed, obsession or addiction which excludes one`s own spiritual development; a development that should involve prayer and consideration for one`s neighbour.

We should obviously enjoy the growth and use of our own talents plus enjoy the products of society but not to such an extent that spiritually we are destroyed. Just as people in ancient times chose to worship other gods so people today can erect their own false gods. It is a danger that can subtley creep up on the best of us, but once recognised it can better be dealt with.

Be positive, think positive, by counting your blessings.

BLESSINGS TO YOU.

If you woke up this morning with more health than illness, you are more blessed than the million who won't survive the week.

If you have never experienced the danger of battle, the loneliness of imprisonment, the agony of torture or the pangs of starvation, you are ahead of 20 million people, around the world.

If you attend a church meeting without fear of harassment, arrest, torture, or death, you are more blessed than almost three billion people in the world.

If you have food in your refrigerator, clothes on your back, a roof over your head and a place to sleep, you are richer than 75% of this world.

If you have money in the bank, in your wallet and spare change in a dish somewhere, you are among the top 8% of the world's wealthy.

If your parents are still married and alive, you are very rare especially in the United States.

If you hold up your head with a smile on your face and are truly thankful you are blessed, because the majority can, but most do not.

If you can hold someone's hand, hug them or even touch them on their shoulder, you are blessed because you can offer God's healing touch.

If you can read this message you are more blessed than over 2 billion people who cannot read anything at all.

You are so blessed in ways you may never have even known. From the Internet.
Reproduced in St. Chad's Parish Magazine, p11, May 2006 by Dee Amos. Sutton Coldfield. U.K.

Where there's life there's still hope.

Live life as simply as possible.

Live to learn and learn to live.

Just enjoy being alive.

You should live by admiration, hope and love. Wordsworth.

The art of living lies in the subtle interchange between activity and rest to produce a pleasurable day; every day.

To see a World in a Grain of Sand, and a Heaven in a Wild Flower, Hold Infinity in the palm of your hand, And Eternity in an hour. Auguries of Innocence, 1. William Blake.

Be sensitive to the world around you.

Behind every concept is a world of knowledge.

"A merry heart does good like a medicine" - Plato.

In helping to heal others, maybe one helps to heal oneself.

A word of encouragement to someone in distress can have a huge effect. Every day look out for opportunities to make someone happy.

121

I've discovered from being ill that small kindnesses do matter.

Give kindness to everyone. You may get many unexpected surprises when they are returned.

Goodwill multiplies.

The full consequences of an act of kindness cannot totally be predicted. They radiate like ripples on a pond.

Everything of worth often comes, at first, from small beginnings.

Just enjoy thinking of all the good things.

If you don't feel comfortable, don't suffer it; change it.

A successful life is more important than a successful career.

Don't cheat on yourself. If you have worked for a reward, let yourself enjoy it.

Every experience is an opportunity to gain wisdom.

Be strong, serene and dignified in the face of your infirmity.

And of the worst pain, this also will pass. Solomon.

Friendship offers a window on the world.

It is heartening to see the silent bravery of so many quite ordinary folk in their struggle in life.

Don't risk all you have - for what may turn out to be a worth-less pursuit.

Enjoy the moment.

PROBLEMS.

Denial and the repression of truth inevitably bring disaster.

Human perceptions are not the truth. A different mood puts a different complexion on your experiences.

They meant the best, but ensured the worst.
(Andrew Sutton).

It can often be the case that in trying to solve a complex problem, be it at a personal or even international level, actions that are meant to help, actually make the situation worse. Help has to be tailored, targeted and then evaluated to see whether it has had the desired effect.

Believe that every problem can be analysed and ameliorated or maybe has at least a partial solution because otherwise no attempt will be made to solve it.

Problem-solving involves defining the problem and then thinking of solutions. (Trower et al. 1988). *Do this for your everyday difficulties.*

There is usually more than one way to solve a problem.

With a problem remember C.A.P. Consider All Possibilities. Edward De Bono.

Many problems have no proven solution, therefore one must always test one's hypothesis over the short and long term.

Walking is very good for thinking about unsolved problems.

If it is not broken - don't fix it.

All through history the ways of truth and love have always won. Gandhi.

I think you should stick with whatever works best.

From the most dreadful situations can arise new development, new hope, new life.

From great debacle often comes resurrection.

LOVE.
Love is the heartbeat of the universe. Verdi, La Traviata.

Love is the noblest achievement of creation.

Love. The only indestructible thing. The only wealth and the only reality.
Elizabeth Goudge. From her book "The Dean's Watch".

Give love to everyone around you.

Love implies trust. This is why when it is betrayed by infidelity it is so devastating.

Learning to love yourself is the first love of all.

Learn to love all of the little everyday things in life.

Life is a mystery. Love is the secret.

WHEN WORKING.
Work to make everyday, an enjoyable day; be as well as possible and then productive. If you frequently have unhappy days, change your ways.

Avoid deadlines and rushing to achieve targets. Relax as much as possible in the activity, get comfortable, so as to conserve your energy. Take regular breaks; this helps achieve the latter.

You can find new strength to overcome adversity if you have faith in God.

Failure makes you feel down, but one success can replace all that, with pleasure.

Always be kind to yourself. If you are not, you run grave risks with your mental health.

Don't indulge in self-punishment.

One of the best things in life is a best friend.

You must expend time and effort to maintain in a happy state, all you hold dear in life; your health, your marriage and family relations. If neglected, they will decay and crumble.

Change people's minds by osmosis - continually, quietly and repeatedly introducing the new idea.

If you want to get someone to do something, set up a sequence of steps from his current position up to the target behaviour and reward each step taken. Make the steps so small he can't seriously object.

Don't tell people your good advice; get them to elicit solutions for themselves by careful questionning of "how" and "what" type.

Remember Joseph's advice- in response to the Pharoah's dream heralding seven years of plenty followed by seven years of famine - to husband resources during the years of plenty ready for the years of famine. The cycles of prosperity and recession are perennial. They affect our physical world and our well-being. But you can prepare for them economically and emotionally by always having something in reserve. Bible, Genesis 41, 29-36.

Having modest realisable aims, ambitions and plans for your life, whatever your circumstances is a good thing.

Judging from the number of sperm your father produces in his lifetime and the number of eggs your mother produces in her lifetime, it can be calculated that the chances of being born with your unique set of genes is 100,000 billion to 1. Your life is surely a magnificent gift.

I was angry with my foe, I kept my wrath, my wrath did grow. I was angry with my friend, I told my wrath, my wrath did end. The Poison Tree. William Blake.

Envy, anger, frustration, aggression; don't live with them. Turn them into love.

You can't easily be nice to anyone when you feel angry.

Victims of crime can feel anger, frustration and aggression. This can marr all other relationships until it fades.

Even when you are well, always give yourself periods in the day when you sit and enjoy the silence.

One lie can lead to many others. Lying to yourself is the worst sin.

You get much more when you give.

Happiness is when all your needs are almost satisfied, leaving enough to strive for, to provide a purpose.

You have to work hard at being happy.

Creativity can be a path to happiness.

You must be vigilant in watching for the development of potential problems in your children and partner in order to deal with them swiftly so as to maintain the happiness of the family and thereby yourself.

Individuals need to avoid spending too much time and energy on their career to the detriment of their relationships with their spouse and family.

It is important to always be aware of what your partner is thinking and feeling. Not to do this is to risk a rift developing in your marriage.

To keep your family and friends be indispensable.

Time spent with your children or grandchildren is a good long term investment.

Be careful about short-term pleasure leading to long-term misery.

Remember the power of partial reinforcement. Being rewarded once or twice occasionally can cause a behaviour to be sustained much more permanently than continuous reinforcement.

Lost opportunities will pass, but new ones always appear.

Most misfortunes can be leavened with humour.

The harder you try, the greater the disappointment if you fail but the sweeter the feeling if you succeed.

The number one priority in life is to look after yourself. Keep well. If you aren't well you can't do anything else.

Giving a small surprise to your child or wife can please them immensely.

Even the longest journey starts with a single step.
Brady. U.S.A. Whitehouse aide.

Criticism can be like poison.

Confidence is everything. Without it you attempt nothing.

Necessity is a great motivator.

Doing something new can bring development and pleasure but also risks problems and failure.
Life can be very miserable without peace of mind. Often you only realize this when you lose it.

*Doing something to someone brings alienation, doing
something for someone brings indebtedness.*

*Everyone has great personal power to hurt or help
other people. The latter gives much pleasure.
Everyday, choose someone to whom to give.*

*Whilst in power over others, do unto them as you
would have them do unto you, because one day they
may have power over you.*

Knowledge is power. Machiavelli.

*If from birth to death, you make, just for
arguments sake, 100 decisions a day concerning your
life, that makes 2.5 million in a lifetime at each of
which a good or bad decision can be made which
influences the direction of your time on earth.*

*If you sometimes avoid telling your relatives your
real feelings, to avoid their judgements, opinions
and the pain these might cause you, this limited
communication may damage these relationships in
future.*

*Don't be bitter about the past; focus on the present
and the future.*

Experience is a brutal teacher, but by God we learn.
Bill Nicholson, author of the screenplay Shadowlands.

We read to know we are not alone.
Bill Nicholson, author of the screenplay Shadowlands.

*There is little pleasure in having no-one to admire
your creation; is this why God created Man?*

*Something I've learned from having C.F.S./M.E. is to
pace myself with all activities. It is a valuable
skill for anyone to have through life.*

*Forgiveness is the ultimate gift one can bestow on
another and in the process the hurt is healed.*

"Least said soonest mended" is very true in marital disputes.

To enhance a relationship with someone it is best done one to one, not in a group.

I am aiming to be always, "invincibly good natured." Sir Colin Davis.

Successes make you clever; your failures make you wise. Rabbi Lionel Blue.

As a baboon can't see its own red bottom, so we can't see our own shortcomings. Hamar Tribe, Ethiopia.

When you are stressed you are less able to give to others, you can only take.

When you are stressed, other mildly irritating stimuli have a greater effect on you.

Some people have to be ill before valuing good health,
poor   before valuing wealth,
unemployed before valuing employment,
failures   before valuing success,
divorced   before valuing wife and family.

We shape each other into what we are.

Success can be a subtle seducer, like the call of the sirens.

People get used to what they have and take it for granted.

Never exhaust yourself completely; you need spare energy to cope with the unexpected.

CHAPTER 2. C.F.S./M.E.

Do not fight against C.F.S./M.E., go with it. Record how much you can do each day and then do enough to feel you've achieved something but little enough to avoid fatigue and symptoms. Only increase what you do very gradually. Keep to a safe routine even if you go on holiday. Tell yourself regularly that you are doing well; be pleased with your modest progress. Avoid having negative thoughts about yourself.

Take comfort in the fact that there are many thousands of people with C.F.S./M.E., whose health is worse than yours. Many successful people have suffered from this illness and gone on to make much recovery, such as Clare Francis, round the world yachts-woman and writer and author Dr.Charles Shepherd.

Relaxation and holding your mind free of all thoughts for a short while can be very refreshing.

I`ve often heard business people say they work hard and play hard. It should be; work hard, play hard, don't relax, get C.F.S./M.E.

Get an early diagnosis of C.F.S./M.E. so you can avoid all exercise early on.

Once C.F.S./M.E. has been diagnosed and medical treatment arranged, there is much patience required in waiting for recovery. There is ample time for much emotional distress in this period and hence the need for psychological (not just medical) strategies to combat it.

Just be pleased with progress day to day and feeling comfortable. It doesn't take long to recover quite alot and be able to do things. Just be patient. Don't think of the months lost. Be grateful for what you have now.

Keep a diary of your activities.

Do less than your daily limit.

When resting think of future activities you are going to enjoy, be it listening to the radio, TV, a short walk, talking with a friend or relaxation.

Be pleased with your own careful management of your illness. It is a great achievement. Allow your success to raise your self-esteem.

RELAPSING.

You may not have relapsed to the beginning. Inch away day by day by resting.

With C.F.S./M.E. the prognosis is good. You can have much recovery. It may not be as bad as you think.

This could be the last relapse.

Be assertive say "no" to risking a relapse.

The more relapses you have suffered the more experience you have to help avoid the next one.

Keep the C.F.S./M.E. rules about not pushing yourself and resting and you wont relapse again.

Be ready to change your plans and cancel things if you get tired or fear a relapse.

Beware of having to fulfill an obligation that risks a relapse.

Avoiding relapses, you can improve.

Be pleased with being able to say you haven't relapsed today.

If you don't feel up to it don't do it, cancel it. That's better than relapsing.

Don't do anything spontaneously, plan all activity, to help avoid a relapse.

If you are careful there is no need to have another relapse or any more pain.

Each relapse however unwelcome, brings with it a new chance to succeed. Don't give up hope.

Don't despair if you are having many relapses. The more you get, the more you know about what causes them and the more you can do to avoid them.

Recovery after a relapse is like a resurrection to new life.

Your greatest fear is of continually relapsing.

It takes time to come to terms with a relapse. It can cause secondary depression.

Be pleased when you have avoided relapsing; that is the most important thing.

When you have a relapse you become upset psychologically. You become angry and want to get back to where you were very quickly. Beware of this, as it can cause a second and multiple relapses.

Remember a relapse also upsets your partner, they need time to compose themselves again.

After being well for a time you can get over-confident and risk a relapse.

When you have relapsed get rid of your anger. Write it down and seek out supportive people to whom you can talk.

Getting your symptoms back raises all the horrible spectre of relapsing. It shatters your confidence again.

After being active, it is hard when a relapse occurs and you have to go back to doing nothing again.

Sex can cause a relapse.

I associate tiredness with relapsing. This is why being tired is so worrying and produces anxiety.

One lives with the daily fear of relapse.

All the good things in life are just waiting for you to get well.

Build up activity in all areas very gradually. Look after your morale.

You have lots of chances to get better. This could be the one.

With C.F.S./M.E. you have the chance to do something different from just going to work.

The pain of being fed up can be lifted by looking forward to getting well, going out, doing your hobbies.

C.F.S./M.E. requires good self-control to get recovery.

Believe you will get better. You can with C.F.S./M.E.

Talk to people who have been as bad as you with C.F.S./M.E. who have got better.

When really down, phone the M.E. Association Help-line.

Try to stop an activity whilst you feel good, not when you feel tired or get symptoms.

Never feel tired, stop before you do.

Eighty-five percent of survival in the wild is psychological - so too is C.F.S./M.E.

Time all activity and increase in small steps.

Be pleasantly surprised by improvements.

You could see big progress in a year; just be patient. This year should be better than last.

Look forward to little things like writing a letter and getting the post.

Losing your independence is a bad thing about C.F.S./M.E. Try to retrieve it alittle when you are well.

With C.F.S./M.E. you inevitable have to be dependent but you can encourage your partner not to be too dominant by saying "oh, I do like it when you consult me and ask for my opinion."

Don't blame yourself for your illness, it is not your fault. You don't deserve it.

When having to lie down, practice relaxation, use a relaxation tape. If you can think without making yourself ill go somewhere nice in your imagination; somewhere you've been on holiday.

When you can get out join your local C.F.S./M.E. support group. You`ll be amazed at the number of people just like you.

The huge support you can get from meeting other sufferers is underestimated.

Lying down isn`t as bad as you think.

Space activity between rests.

Don`t lose heart - things will improve. It wont be long before you feel lovely again.

Compare yourself with other ailing people - having C.F.S./M.E. isn't as bad as some illnesses. You haven't got cancer or anything terminal.

Just being intensely passive and you can get better. You don't have to do anything.

A cure or more effective treatment maybe is only months away.

If you are able to think without making yourself ill, then mentally write your autobiography including your ordeal with C.F.S./M.E.

In the frustration of this illness don't be too passive or aggressive with other people - be assertive of your views. Plainly and firmly speak your mind - you`ll feel better for it.

Remember that for some people with C.F.S./M.E. thinking hard can produce symptoms as well as physical work.

Be gentle with C.F.S./M.E. and it will be gentle with you.

Some small improvement could come later today or tomorrow.

It is good if you haven't got worse.

Find people who will listen to you; often the best are other people with C.F.S./M.E. If necessary telephone them.

Every day should be better than the day before.

At least when ill it sharpens the pleasure of living when you are well.

Continually look for any small improvement.

If you aren't sure you have the energy to do something postpone it until a bit later.

Remember progress can be erratic and uneven.

Talking incessantly about C.F.S./M.E. helps to cope with it; but be careful of your carer becoming satiated with it.

Don't alienate any of your family through talking too much about your illness.

Evidence of a little progress can give you a real lift.

Reading the notes of past recovery can raise your hopes.

Gradual recovery is very rewarding. Hang on, a cure isn't that far away.

Hope, above all else is what you need.

Keep within your limits and life will gradually revive and blossom again like a flower opening in the sunshine.

Everyone with C.F.S./M.E. often feels low after a great deal of resting; don't let it spoil your enjoyment.

Encourage your partner or family to say to you 'We love you, you are getting better. It wont be long."

Even people with C.F.S./M.E. can be enterprising and learn new skills little by little.

There is life after C.F.S./M.E.

Over-excitement can cause symptoms.

In her book "Forever Tomorrow" Jessie Hunt says of being ill with cancer; "if you keep yourself cheerful and think `I'm going to get better, its not going to beat me` your good cells stay healthy. But if you start to think `I don't feel well, I don't think I'll get over it` then the bad cells get stronger and the good cells become weaker. Make up your mind it is going to be alright." This could be the same with C.F.S/M.E.

Turn every experience of C.F.S./M.E. to spiritual profit.

Look for a way for personal growth through your experience of C.F.S./M.E.

C.F.S./M.E. shatters your confidence to do anything. As you get well, build it back by achieving little targets.

You inevitably become subordinate in your relationships.

When you feel better you can become alittle more assertive.

There is a constant battle between needing to rest and wanting to do something. Doing just a few minutes of a pleasurable activity can lift your spirits.

As your fatigue subsides, mentally you begin to feel better. You can think better thoughts.

When having to rest, use the time to think in detail about what you want to do in your activity time no matter how short. Look forward to it.

Resting isn't a waste of time; you are helping yourself to get better.

Remember that even listening to the radio can be tiring.

If a job is too daunting to do all at once, break it down into parts small enough to be completed with satisfaction. Remember the lady of 70 with C.F.S./M.E. who decorated her room doing it 10 minutes at a time each day. It took her two years but she did it!

C.F.S./M.E. means less control over your life. Reduced autonomy means more stress.

Dependency is worrying. The answer is to relearn skills when you are able.

The psychological component of C.F.S./M.E. is the most important part, because your attitude influences your response to your illness and that in turn your well-being.

Remember C.F.S./M.E. tends to gradually get better with time.

Be careful of continually moaning to your partner who cares for you. You can generate "compassion fatigue" in friends and relatives. Often you do it for the reassurance that is given to you.

Remember your challenge in life at the moment is to overcome C.F.S./M.E.

The trial of C.F.S./M.E. has taught me how patient and kind my wife is. I never fully realised what beautiful qualities she had until now. This might be the same for your partner.

When getting well, don't be greedy and do too much.

The price of freedom from C.F.S./M.E. is eternal vigilance against doing too much.

Be very flexible. Always cancel an event if you don't feel up to it. You can always do it some other time.

Reflect on the good achievements in your life so far. It is an antidote to the feeling of uselessness you sometimes get in doing nothing for so long. Think positively and look for progress in your condition.

Beware that your illness does not make you bitter and twisted. It can.

Sometimes you can feel so well that you don't deserve it; but you do, you deserve all the happiness you can get.

Remember your partner suffers the effects and restrictions of C.F.S./M.E. as you the sufferer do.

Every morning I have woken and for a moment felt the bliss and the freedom of being without C.F.S./M.E. before the memory comes flooding back.

As you get better all your pleasures will gradually be returned to you.

As you get better hopes and aspirations come closer to being realised. There is a subtle change and improvement of attitude.

Don't worry about what you have lost through C.F.S./M.E., think about what pleasures there might be in the future.

A lady called Mina Keel took up music composition again after 46 years. In the same way there is life after C.F.S./M.E. Just be patient.

In a similar way I was unable to read or write because of C.F.S./M.E. for two years, but after that I gradually increased it to the present level of up to 7 hours per day.

Time goes by inexorably. Every day you can feel a little better.

After months of resting and doing nothing, activity is a huge pleasure. You value more than ever, getting you life back, bit by bit.

As you get better you can do more reading and writing of letters, therefore you get more letters in the post. Being able to read again you can buy magazines and newspapers and take more interest in life generally.

Since you can't do much with C.F.S./M.E. you do have time to listen to people in coffee bars talking about themselves. There are many people who are glad of someone to talk to and to listen to them. It can be very pleasurable for you too. Set out to go for a coffee in a coffee shop and have a conversation with someone.

I have gone from having nearly every moment in my life organised when in a job, down to having all the time in the world to do nothing.

Don't let C.F.S./M.E. spoil your personality.

Relatives can be upset by your C.F.S./M.E. and respond by being aggressive, angry and unpleasant to you. Tell them that they are upsetting you. Tell them how they can help you.

Look for the positive things that have come out of having C.F.S./M.E., i.e. nearness to God, learning to value your close family, valuing life itself.

The most successful thing you have ever done, is to live through this C.F.S./M.E. You are still in with a chance.

If you can't read because of C.F.S./M.E. get your partner to tell you the main stories of the day from the newspaper. This can be very pleasing.

With C.F.S./M.E. I feel after I have enjoyed myself greatly, I half expect to be punished because that's what usually happens.

If you have coped with C.F.S./M.E. you must have alot of grit. Be proud of this.

Looking forward to improvement and better times is an antidote to being fed up.

Getting very tired seems to promote anxiety. Rest and relaxation is the solution.

Don't be angry when a little job takes longer than you expected. Better to stop and finish it tomorrow rather than risk getting symptoms or a relapse.

If you don't have the energy to do what you want today, there is always tomorrow.

The worst thing with this illness is to feel bitter and resentful that you have it. You will upset yourself grievously.

Take comfort in talking with other C.F.S./M.E. sufferers.

The best way to help and please your partner is to stay well.

After a while everyone expects you to have coped with C.F.S./M.E. without any trouble. In reality everyday is a struggle to avoid emotional pain.

I used to dread anyone asking me to do something for them, if it was unexpected, as it might make me tired or relapse.

Retirement and C.F.S./M.E. have meant a reduced income, loss of self-esteem and status in society and in my family. Work and income are the principal means by which men maintain their self-esteem. Lack of them has caused me emotional pain. I try to combat this by writing and remembering that I do work, if only part-time.

One of the most debilitating aspects of C.F.S./M.E. is that you no longer have to make the effort to do anything. You can happily do nothing from getting up to going to bed. You lose all confidence to do things.

C.F.S./M.E. dominates your whole life. Every minute of the day you must assess what will be the effect on your illness, of doing something.

What you lose in spontaneity you gain in anticipation.

Giving yourself a complete day off all activity and resting more than usual can give you a boost of energy the following day I find.

You need to read optimistic literature about C.F.S./M.E.

You can sometimes envy other C.F.S./M.E. sufferers getting better quicker than yourself.

When you get tired you fear getting the symptoms of a relapse again. It haunts you till the symptoms subside.

My wife checks with me that I haven't walked too far or done too much. She means well but it makes me feel like a child. However it must be good if it helps avoid a relapse.

If you keep a diary you notice that C.F.S./M.E. becomes very predictable, which is a blessing.

With C.F.S./M.E. there seems to be alot of waiting in life.

Show infinite patience in the face of C.F.S./M.E.

C.F.S./M.E. stopped me in my tracks. I had a fast way of life. Now I reflect on everything I do.

It is not always obvious why you feel fed up. It can be because of the feelings of frustration due to the restrictions of the illness. Talking it out with someone can help find the reason.

It takes courage to keep gently pushing up your performance and activity. It would be easy to relax into comfortable indolence.

The anxiety you fear, is worry about having to do something you feel you might not cope with because of fatigue.

As you get better you can gradually increase your ambitions.

Watching TV programmes with humour and happy endings can lift you alot. Read books that have happy endings. Avoid negative, unhappy material and depressing TV news programmes.

Getting better can be a problem in coming to terms with the change it implies for both you the sufferer and your carer,i.e. having to get ready to work part-time, being less dependent etc.

Before I improved, I missed going to work and taking part in society.

I worry that my intelligence has been compromised by my illness.

I sometimes feel surprised when I'm not tired.

Don't push yourself you might lose what you already have.

Don`t be frightened to take part in the great cycle of life even with C.F.S./M.E. Do what you can.

Don't fight C.F.S./M.E. head on, be subtle clever, work round it. Beat it with guile.

You don't really understand anything until you have experienced it yourself. This is true of this illness and much of human experience.

When you have to give up your favourite activities to rest, enjoy selecting other more passive things to do whilst you recover (ie reading or the video).

Hate and anger at C.F.S./M.E. will destroy you; loving keeps you alive.

I am sure my brain has been damaged by C.F.S./M.E. Too much analytical thinking causes me headaches and hypoglycaemic symptoms. In the past it has taken weeks of refraining from mental activity to resolve them but even these improve.

I appear "not with it" because C.F.S./M.E. leaves you less mental energy to rehearse what everyone is doing. Tranquillizers make thinking slow and exacerbate the problem. Forward planning without a diary is a problem.

Tranquillisers also seem to dampen loving feelings. I have found they reduce your ability to love.

Symptoms of C.F.S./M.E. caused by excessive mental activity are sometimes due to hypoglycaemia and relieved by eating.

Getting hungry causes low blood sugar which then causes adrenalin to liberate more glucose from cells and the adrenalin can make you feel anxiety. Eating resolves it.

With C.F.S./M.E. you can forget what it's like to feel vital, fit and physically exhilarated.

Once you start to accept your illness and your limitations and enjoy the limited life you have - a great peace grows in you that brings joy to all that you are able to do.

Sometimes you need to rest in complete quiet for a time. Listening to music or the radio can be tiring.

If you are getting tired and unwell, quickly consider dropping from full-time to part-time work. This could help avoid having to stop work altogether.

Knowing that C.F.S./M.E. exists, makes you worry that every little cold or flu your family get is going to be C.F.S./M.E. We couldn't cope if another member of the family got C.F.S./M.E.

The danger is that physical activity gives you a lovely feeling but with C.F.S./M.E. the terrible consequences come later. If you aren't sure how tired you are, lie down and see how long it takes you to recover.

When the water pump and tap in my caravan needed replacing the man at the caravan centre said it was an easy job to replace. Not wanting to appear a wimp at DIY I decided to do the job myself. For 1 hour 20 minutes spread over the day I struggled, using many muscles, to do the repair. Afterwards I feared I would get repercussions of anxiety, muscle tingling or relapse in the coming days. I had risked everything, breaking my own rules. I had been "sucked in" and trapped into doing more than I felt capable of. Fortunately I didn't relapse.

Very mild exercise in a game like table tennis of short duration is excellent for boosting one's feeling of well being.

Tingling in my muscles warns me that I have done enough or even too much.

You are at your most vulnerable when you try to do more.

If you feel tired never push yourself.

Having C.F.S./M.E. you can not feel confident about coping with sudden unplanned extra demands.

After working, rest until the fatigue has completely cleared before you start work again.

Setbacks serve to remind you that you are never likely to be totally free of this illness.

Having aches and pains can make you feel tired.

With this illness you cannot easily cope with outstanding unsolved problems or any stress.

If you've done too much and fear a relapse, noticing whether the fatigue changes from uncomfortable to pleasant will indicate whether you are likely to relapse. If the fatigue becomes pleasant it is unlikely.

To change your life even with C.F.S./M.E. do the 6 Ps.

1.   Plan. Have a plan of what you really want to do. Decide the target and work out the steps back to where you are now. Reward each step achieved.

2.   Positive. Be positive. Clear out all the hinderances to change.

3.   Predict success. Expect to succeed.

145

4. Power. A good self-esteem gives you the power to do things, therefore love yourself.

5. Please yourself. Have fun doing it.

6. Pace. Take the first step.

* * *

CHAPTER 3. CHRONIC ILLNESS.

BE POSITIVE.

Thinking positive thoughts can actually make you feel better, less depressed.

Try to avoid being very fed up; try to think positively and look forward to treats in store. Do something pleasurable for two or three minutes.

You can fill a lot of time in relaxation and saying positive self statements to yourself; i.e. saying good things about yourself.

Be positive and joyful, don't be downhearted.

I know it can be hard to but try and be positive.

You probably sometimes feel angry at being ill. Counter this by thinking of the positives things in your life.

Enjoy positive fantasies not negative ones.

Avoid all stress and deadlines for work and activity.

There is huge relief when the symptoms subside.

Enjoy the sharpness and pleasure of feeling well, when it happens.

To avoid feeling useless, one can always listen to others and their problems.

Because of the vicissitudes of illness, paradoxically you can have more time to spend on yourself than ever before.

Do not set any deadlines by which you have to get better. Let the healing go at its own pace.

Remember you may have passed the worst.

Don't give up yet as much recovery could be just around the corner.

Cut back what you do for a while, if you get any symptoms.

Write down a list of thoughts that please you and think of them whenever you have the need.

Be happy when your loved-ones come to see you.

Keep a record of all you do in a day to help stay on an even keel, and avoid the ups and downs.

Take one day at a time. Take every opportunity to enjoy all you can, even a cup of tea or a short talk with a friend on the phone.

Have something, however small, to look forward to every hour.

Being in pain emphasizes the pleasure of being pain-free when it comes.

If thoughts can make you ill they can also make you better.

You can influence your future by how you think and pray. Your thoughts predispose you to a particular destiny.

When on holiday keep to the same daily total. Don't be tempted to do more.

Being satisfied with your health and activity for the present gives peace of mind.

Please your partner by being joyful when you are well.

When you are well, be a pleasure to be with; spread sunshine and happiness around you.

Be grateful for feeling as well as you do.

Reward yourself regularly, you deserve it.

Don't bottle up your feelings, find someone to tell. Let them out. If you feel like crying, cry and you'll feel better afterwards.

Try to do something, no matter how small for someone else. It will make you feel good and useful.

Reward you partner when s/he loves you.

Listen to your favourite music as a little reward.

Plan to make and enjoy little purchases when you can get out to the local shops or ask someone to get them for you.

Think what you are going to do today, tomorrow and in future and take pleasure in these thoughts.

Don't let illness destroy what you already have.

Chronic illness has lead me to discover that something I really wanted, I already had; love.

Don`t get envious of others, it only hurts you.

Remember to take pride in your achievements, past and present.

Foster and encourage good feelings in yourself.

Just as you cannot be anxious when you are relaxed, you cannot be fed up or have bad thoughts like envy, jealousy or hatred when you love.

Avoid becoming angry with yourself; never punish yourself because of your lack of energy or short-comings.

Don't let others including doctors punish you.

Try to reward those closest to you; let them know when you are feeling good; let them experience the pleasure as well.

If you have learnt something from your pain and adversity, not all of it has been in vain.

Try to be at peace with yourself. Give love to everyone. Love begets joy. Have joy.

After every debacle, there is a resurrection.

List all the activities you CAN DO, like listening to music the radio TV videos, writing, reading, sleeping, relaxation, daydreaming, walking in the garden, looking at holiday photo-albums.

Make a list of good things to think about.

The aim is inner-peace and tranquility, free from pain and mental anguish. Be grateful for this.

What you think does affect how you feel.

Don't think ahead too far when ill. Just take a day at a time.

Beware of feeling well and being tempted to do too much.

Try to keep well within your limits.

If you have to rest alot, lie on different beds in different bedrooms. Different houses can be fun.

Get everyone to give you lots of encouragement. Give them a rewarding comment when they do.

Think about what you will do when you are well enough, ie. holidays, buying things, sex.

When your friends and relatives ask how they can help you, tell them just to listen, to give no unsolicited advice and to give lots of encouragement.

Look for reward in, seeing and talking to people, in a cup of tea, feeling no symptoms, feeling comfortable, in good news, in flowers growing in *your garden, in a sugar-free sweet and in your little achievements.*

Keep smart, take a pride in your appearance, it gives you a lift though I know it isn't easy.

Treat yourself to some new clothes when you can.

When you are suffering, remember the sweetness of the times when you were well, they can come again.

Listen and take notice of your body.

RELAXATION

Use relaxation to control anxiety; using a relaxation tape can be very helpful.

Remember that relaxation and resting always help to improve the symptoms.

Resting is more pleasurable when you have no symptoms.

To remain symptom-free and feeling well is the most important thing.

Be of indomitable spirit.

Build activity in very small steps; this builds your confidence as well.

Take every opportunity to enjoy all the little things in daily life.

Treat yourself, value yourself, love yourself.

Use your grit and determination to stay well within your limits.

Be assertive in defence of yourself. Don't let others coerce you into overdoing it.

When you feel really desperate, do relaxation and in your thoughts go somewhere really nice. Have pleasant thoughts and plan a nice activity to do next even if it is only for a few minutes.

Plan your day carefully to avoid overdoing it.

Rest at quiet times so that you have energy for when your family are around.

Often activities have to be broken down into very small parts to be done over a long time. Be patient in this endeavour.

Light activity and progress are an anti-depressant against feeling low.

Forget the trials of yesterday, think how to get a good day today.

Remember that, from suffering can come love, patience and wisdom.

When you are experiencing pleasure you can't experience pain.

Take sustinence from the heroic courage shown by other people suffering pain and discomfort.

Don't give up on your hopes and dreams.

When you have to cancel some activities you have looked forward to, enjoy rescheduling them for another day.

If you have had a setback it may not be as bad as you think.

Be pleased with each day you survive.

Let the love of your partner, children and family fill you with life-giving balm. Feel the power of it.

List all the treasures you have on earth.

Don't be bitter or envious of other people it only hurts you yourself in the end. Banish such thoughts from your mind.

"I carry my own hell within me." Orpheus from Orpheus and Eurydice. An opera by Gluck.

If you are in any doubt whether an action is good or bad - abstain from it. Zorasta: Persia.

Listen to your body, it might have a message for you.

A hug from a loved one can really lift your spirits.

When you have enough to do, you must say "no" to every subsequent suggestion for new activity.

If you have the philosophy that you cannot do anything to improve your illness or well-being, you can make the mistake of giving up, and making no effort to get better. This is learned helplessness.

Remember to praise your partner who cares for you frequently. Make it a pleasure to look after you. The best reward you can give them is to be joyful.

Boost your morale by saying to yourself that you are not as badly off as some people.

The most important thing is to keep your hope and optimism.

Put bird-feeders in your garden and watch the birds come and go from a comfortable chair by a window. It is brilliant.

CARERS.

When I'm relapsed and can't go out or on holiday, my wife, being the carer has nothing to look forward to and she feels miserable.

Dissent between you and your carer can be very upsetting, therefore avoid it as much as possible. Nothing really matters that much.

Encourage your partner to spend some time making him or herself look good. This can give you immense pleasure.

Remember the carer needs to reward themself frequently throughout the day. They deserve it for the way they are coping with what they have to put up with. They should say "well done I am doing well."

The carer needs to be strong for both themselves and the sufferer.

It is not always good for the carer to do all of a sufferer`s chores, because this removes the anti-depressant effect of some activity and totally deprives them of their role in their family. Encourage them to do what they can. Then praise them whole-heartedly.

Any progress made by the sufferer is very pleasing for the carer.

A carer, to look after someone may have to reduce their own personal goals in life for a time. This can risk producing a melancholy mood or depression.

Being a carer is anxiety-provoking and tiring, especially if the sufferer's illness is unpredictable and precludes future planning.

The improving health of the sufferer diminishes the role of the carer. Not all carers are accepting of this.

It really hurts when the partner who is the carer wants to start making plans which leave you, the invalid, out. E.g. going on holiday without you.

Don't underestimate how depressing and demoralizing it can be for a carer looking after an ill person.

Carers are often unsung heroes.

Receiving unsolicited advice, it is suggested, is irksome because it implies, you need advice because you are lacking in some way. This implication can possibly lower your self-esteem, and perhaps this is why such advice can be unwelcome.

NEW ROLES.
If you have no other useful role, you can easily take on that of a counsellor to your friends, relatives and their children. All you have to do to be a brilliant counsellor is to listen uncritically to people as they relate their problems. Anyone can do this for anyone else and it is the most precious gift one person can give to another. The joy is in the fact that anyone even with chronic illness can do this in conversation with anyone else and feel the pleasure of doing something good.

Be the family facilitator, help things to happen, to assist your spouse and children.

Try to avoid rewarding undesirable behaviour in others.

Be a rewarding person to be with.

Remember that you can still reward people with your behaviour. We all have a huge reservoir of pleasing responses.

"Give sincere praise whenever and where ever possible. Loving praise towards another person is highly therapeutic for both the person receiving the praise and for the person giving the praise". Gordon A. Hendry.

Even though chronically ill, remember you still have the power to make people feel good.

If you do nothing else your role could be to just be a good person.

Everyone regardless of the extent of their illness can attempt to fulfill the simple role of just trying to help other people. This could be your role in life if nothing else. It is a worthy aim.

Sometimes in the hurly-burly of life it is paradoxically the one who is chronically ill who has the time to give to everyone encountered. Look out for little ways in which you can please people. This could be one of your roles in life.

Kindness generates indebtedness. This can be a useful source of personal credit when negotiating socially.

Accruing wisdom is something anyone can do.

Just because you have the capability does not mean you have to use it.

It takes much self-control to stop doing something you enjoy when you know you have done enough. Try to stop before you feel fatigued or get symptoms.

Think over what you have done today, however small. This can be very pleasing.

Don't be greedy in your quest for pleasure and improvement. Be patient.

Anyone can be driven to think of committing suicide given enough pain and anguish. If you ever need them, don't forget the Samaritans (tel: *08457-90-90-90.*

In this illness, I have suffered more pain than I ever thought possible, but eventually it resolved.

Having a little manageable project in hand that you enjoy doing gives you something to think about and gives you a lift e.g. writing, art, making greetings cards from a kit, sewing etc.

Lots of people get into emotional turmoil, but they get out of it. You will.

No matter how well you feel, stick to your rules.

Be careful of punishing your partner's efforts to cheer you up by remaining miserable.

I feel brilliant when my wife praises me for making a bit of progress. Get your partner to do the same for you.

I love it when my wife comes to give me a hug. Reciprocate with your own partner when this happens.

Be a pleasure to be with, delight and please people with your company. This can be your role for the time-being.

Remember your partner can become weary and tired emotionally trying to cope with your illness. Give them space to recover. Allow them respite and you will see the benefit.

Think about what you can do, not what you can't.

Beware of people being insensitive about your illness and your limitations; like not being able to go on holiday or being retired and not working. Many can be. It is probably just thoughtlessness.

When ill, some people try to help you even when you don't want it. You seem to have less rights when you are ill.

Beware of feeling you are just waiting to die. Try to do things which are useful to the family or yourself.

Beware of buying or having to learn something new. That can be worrying. Break the job down into small parts and use relaxation to assuage anxiety.

You now know what it is like to be chronically ill. On the positive side you now have an insight into many other distressing conditions.

With feared or anxiety-provoking situations, get completely relaxed lying down and imagine going through the situation - whilst remaining completely relaxed.

The chances are, things will be a bit better tomorrow.

Anxiety can be a signal that you have done enough or too much.

Feel the confidence of knowing you are within your limits.

Remember your partner needs support as well as you. Look out for supportive friends and relatives.

Knowledge learnt in suffering is the truth.

There is pleasure in just feeling well.

When you are ill, you receive, all the time. It is nice to sometimes "give".

Take pleasure in all the events of your family. Be magnanimous.

Don`t suffer in silence. Tell your relatives how you feel - good and bad.

I greatly miss my old job but I have tried to replace it with similar activities.

I sometimes get fed up with being told what to do all the time "rest, sit down, don't do too much".

Your partner can become like a one-parent family getting used to taking all the decisions without you. Try to take part in decision-making as much as possible.

Being envious of other people's good health only gives you heart-ache.

You have to be happy yourself before you can make others happy.

Hardship in life is to teach you not to be hard-hearted.

Being optimistic makes it more likely things will go well.

Remember that suffering enables you to appreciate the pleasures, even the small ones, so much more.

Those who have suffered, are more likely to be spiritually ahead of those who have not.

Diversify your sources of pleasure, so that they occur ever hour or so.

Your suffering isn't wasted, because it strengthens your character and makes you a more compassionate person.

At the end of a day reflect on what you have achieved or improved and be pleased with it no matter how small.

Music especially joyful hymns can lift your spirits.

Forgive yourself and others for all that has gone wrong in the past.

Sympathetic support is essential for recovery.

Don't let other people's achievements belittle the value you place on your own.

Remember even now you are achieving spiritually.

I have had so much emotional pain that I felt that I didn't deserve happiness. I feared losing it when it occurred. However it passed.

When getting symptoms you feel you can't cope with any change or anything new.

You don't help anyone by giving so much of yourself that you are exhausted.

I found having to describe the history of my illness to a doctor for the first time very upsetting in having to go over all my pain again. It took time to recover.

God is on the side of the suffering. He seeks to bring good out of all tragedy. He is by your side always.

One of the most enjoyable activities is meeting and talking with other people.

Poverty is oppressive. You feel guilty taking pleasure in buying little luxuries.

In talking to people you often don't get passed the "small talk" but when talking to someone with the same problem you soon get on to talking about your real feelings.

I feel low when I compare myself to my peers and their promotion and salaries.

Sometimes relatives think I am fed up in order to get attention. This is not true.

Talking about my real feelings helps.

Fear of the future - being unable to care for yourself and having to go into a home - is not uncommon.

Telling yourself you are doing well, often enough and you begin to believe it.

You can feel guilty letting the rest of the family do everything for you.

You can feel angry with being ill.

Continually pushing yourself - slows down recovery.

I worry my wife will go off me now I have lost status.

Helping to do the children's homework helped raise self-esteem and status in the family for me. I felt useful.

Be happy to sit comfortably and be free of pain.

Being on less money you can feel guilty spending anything. It is a horrible feeling of restriction. And at one time I could do no work to get better off. I now understand better how the poor feel.

Lying down so much, one begins to live life vicariously through TV and your own imagination and thought. In this state the telephone and car are a life-line.

When my wife gets tired she worries more, which affects me. You and your partner are inextricably bound together emotionally.

Looking at and holding the book that I wrote and had published, before having to retire, greatly pleases me. It reminds me of my career.

The way you think about your symptoms when they come can make them seem much worse and this can lead to feeling very miserable. Look at your symptoms in the most optimistic way you can as this makes you feel better.

Look after yourself, be careful.

When you get symptoms you worry they will never subside. They will.

You need someone to boost your confidence by saying you are coping better. My wife does this for me all the time. Not everyone can do this for you.

Remember 9 out of 10 ailments improve after resting the affected area.

You get more done when taking regular breaks.

It often takes more courage to carry on living than to die.

It can be very frustrating having to stop an activity before it is finished in order to keep to your limits, but it pays off immensely in the end.

Having something to look forward to, improves the quality of life in the intervening months for both you and your partner. It could be a holiday, a visit, or something to buy.

When you improve, it will be nice to live with less worry.

I used to panic when the phone rang in case someone wanted me to do something.

When you've been ill you fear getting everyone else's illness.

If you gave into the fear of things happening, you'd do nothing. Life functions because most of the time most things go OK.

Intellectual achievement can give huge pleasure.

You can often be upset and made to feel fed up by very small things.

There is a chain of activity. One interest leads to others. My desire to write requires a computer and printer and this fed my interest in computer magazines, business computing and shopping, saving my money and making special purchases; then teaching my children how to use the computer. I know someone *who is typing up his autobiography, principally to give to his grandchildren.*

Fulfilling activity is one of the best antidotes to being depressed.

Working at home I do miss the interaction with colleagues. However, I have purposely built a new network of friends.

Loving your enemies is the only way, because by hating them you destroy yourself.

Just listening to your partner's worries can help alleviate them. Be a good listener.

Getting a safe daily routine is vital for your psychological well-being. It takes the anxiety out of living.

Beware that other people may envy the time you have for yourself and do not realise the price you have paid.

Being ill is very frustrating when you can't work to get out of poverty.

Time being ill need not be wasted. You can use the period for spiritual development.

As a reward I treat myself to special thoughts about something I want to do or buy.

Even a 5 minute walk each day can brighten your mood.

Buying a single piece of fruit instead of chocolate or sweets can be a treat.

Every day I am pleased if I have managed myself well enough to avoid getting tired.

I sometimes feel I can't enjoy myself because you aren't supposed to when you are ill. Or I feel guilty if I do have a little pleasure.

Parents do not expect to learn from their children, but sometimes life has made them wiser.

We had to adapt to my incapacity with my wife taking all the decisions and then she had to re-adapt to me becoming fitter and more independent.

Enjoy hearing people's news and gossip.

Don't give up hope, you just never know what good things are around the corner.

Remember Kafka's story about the Great Wall of China. No one wanted to build it in one go, but plenty of people agreed to build it in thousands of one mile sections. Franz Kafka "The Great Wall of China. Metamorphosis and Other stories. Penguin:

Little acquaintances can be very rewarding.

When you feel well yourself - you can be more generous to other people.

The hardest time to be patient is when you feel well.

After doing nothing for years it takes some effort to cope with a more complicated life.

Survival is about diversity of thought and attitude.

When you have made some progress it is nice to tell people some good news when they ask.

Light is stronger than darkness - hold onto the light and it will see you through. Terry Waite.

If you cannot progress, think well of what you have achieved and look forward to what you can do in the future.

There is a fine line between excitement and looking forward to something and being anxious and dreading it.

Activity makes the time when you relax more pleasurable.

When you are ill you become dependent and can lose some of your status and power in the family. You are in a lesser negotiating position which is hard to change when you get well. When you are ill you fear disapproval. You can't cope with anyone's negative feelings towards you.

If you haven't suffered much illness in life, being chronically ill and disabled may be very hard to cope with if it happens.

You only realise the true worth of your partner when they are there for you when things are going badly.

When pain stops, rejoicing begins.

It is only when you try to achieve, that you increase your chances of success.

Once you are chronically ill you sometimes can fear further illnesses later in life.

You can get huge pleasure from coming together in a community of people in a church, society, club or class.

Anxiety makes problems seem worse, more complicated and more difficult to cope with than they are in reality. The solution is careful, thorough preparation and simulated trials with small-step, increasingly close, approximations to the ultimate task.

Plan all of your household activities to cost the minimum of effort; such as the garden, washing, meals i.e. cook casseroles which cook whilst you can rest.

Seeing a good film with a happy ending gives you a boost and pleasant food for thought.

Always be aware of behaving in a way that cannot be sustained.

When satiated with one task, try another that uses a different set of muscles and you may find that you have more energy by doing this, i.e. switching from reading or writing to walking.

When doing any activity don't rush as this tenses muscles unnecessarily and causes premature fatigue.

Doing your tasks deliberately very slowly in a very unhurried fashion greatly increases the pleasure derived and cuts down fatigue. It also takes no more time than rushing.

Find a relaxing position for doing a task and prolong your working time before fatiguing.

It is a constant battle to avoid rushing.

Do the demanding work first and the routine later.

If you lose something, you have got to appreciate what is left.

"Do what works". President Roosevelt.

Look out for kindred spirits.

Avoid becoming totally self absorbed in your own illness to the exclusion of all concern about other people's needs. You will become self-centred and isolated.

Be careful you don't learn to talk about your illness in order to get people's attention.

When you get symptoms and feel ill you easily forget all the times you were well.

Age is no barrier to friendship.

Delight in giving your family quality time to exchange the day's news.

Being able to do a few activities enables you to have some news to exchange with other people and to take part in pleasant conversation. Remember to ask people what they have been doing this week.

Psychology is the power to bring the best out of people. Use it.

The world's social life is filled by the constant exchange of fascinating tales. Everyone has their own story to tell. Be proud of yours.

Stories are the life-blood of social relations.

We have an insatiable desire to hear other people's stories.

No one is totally in control of their life. Chance still plays a part.

Good memories are important. Cultivate them.

List all the little jobs you can do about the house for your family, e.g. setting the table for a meal, listening to children read, helping with homework or making a cup of tea.

Knowledge is like light; the more you have, the clearer the situation becomes.

"Suffering can have great value. It can enrich our spirituality and deepens our empathy towards others to a degree that nothing else can". Gordon A. Hendry.

Alternating even two boring jobs can give satisfaction.

Just because you have the power to do something, does not mean you have to exercise it.

Sometimes doing nothing is the best course of action.

In the incredible complexity of life, often as one door closes others open.

Crying is an attempt to cope with the unbelievable.

If you have a problem that you can't solve, lying down, relaxing and letting it drift through your mind, can often inspire a solution.

It's never too late to learn. You are never too old to learn.

Never give up; you just don`t know what good things the future holds.

In coping with any misfortune like bereavement or loss of any kind, it is best not to get over-tired. This greatly exacerbates the problem.

If you get concerned about any symptoms, time how long they last.

Pain distorts the perception of the passage of time.

Having the time to sit and do nothing, sometimes can be very pleasurable.

The simplest effective treatment is to avoid getting worse.

Being dependent on Government benefits is very unsettling and worrying. You are not in control of your finances and never know when they will be curtailed. The solution is to have financial reserves as high as possible.

Being chronically ill is incredibly frustrating, since there is so much motivating media-stimulation and consequently so much you want to accomplish. But the over-riding principle is to always work in a sustainable way.

When chronically ill, don't give up all family activities. If you can't swim you can still go with the family to the baths and whilst they swim you can have a coffee and watch from the lounge. If you can't walk for long you can still go to the park with the family but walk for a shorter time or sit down.

168

If you don't have the energy to walk round town, you can have a drink in a coffee bar whilst your partner shops.

When you are ill you feel like punishing yourself for your inadequacies. Don't.

When you are chronically ill you feel angry you can't take part in society.

Every small improvement brings you closer to being able to earn some money.

No matter how hard you try, you can't avoid having the occasional setback. Don't blame or punish yourself for this.

When you are getting symptoms it is hard to remain equable.

When you are well it is much easier to be magnanimous.

When you are chronically ill you forget how people with normal illnesses recover in just a few days.

You are marvellous the way you have coped with your illness. You are still here.

From the most disasterous circumstances can come survival and new life. Never give up hope.

You need to actively look after your morale.

Having chronic illness is exactly like trying to survive in the wild. You don't know whether there will be an end to it.

Reflect on and be pleased with what you have coped with already. Sustain yourself with love. Pace yourself.

Break the ordeal of your illness down into small manageable parts. Take one part at a time, or one day at a time.

In coping with your chronic illness you are as brave as any war hero.

Almost anything is possible if you believe.

I have discovered that some music and operas can give an overwhelming feeling of well-being.

In quietness and confidence shall be your strength.

Weakness besides evincing sympathy can attract aggression.

Strive to be honourable in all matters.

Anticipation enhances pleasure.

Daydreaming can be fun.

Stress comes from not being in control. Having some autonomy over your work and life reduces stress.

Being ill is not very attractive. Try to be presentable. It will raise your morale and that of your partner and family.

Recently I have been well enough to look after my wife when she was ill. Now I know how dispiriting it is seeing her unwell and not having the power to speed her recovery. However, it is nice to be in charge of the shopping and the household. Also, I've discovered how draining it is making the constant effort to support her.

Be assertive with your relatives about the help you want whilst you are ill.

Working to a routine means you don't have to think.

CRISES.
What really disrupts your plans for balancing work and rest is having an unsolved problem on your mind. You tend not to want to stop to rest and when you do stop, you carry on thinking about it.

I've found that in the worst crisis, a good laugh and a joke helps you cope.

Coping in a crisis gives you huge reward.

Being a housewife is like running your own family business, I've discovered.

In a crisis write down your plans; don't try to remember them all; this only causes constant mental rehearsal which is exhausting.

Keep to your usual routine.

The worst time in a crisis is on first waking in the morning when you remember your problem.

Your worries can also come in the middle of the night. Be patient and by mid-morning they will diminish.

When my wife was ill in hospital I had some dysfunctional non-coping beliefs and suicidal fantasies but cognitive behavioural counselling to myself got rid of them completely.

Coping in a crisis gives you more confidence to cope with and enjoy further challenges.

Don't put up your daily work limits during a crisis. Stick to the usual amount.

You can worry you cannot keep up the pace forever. Decide that today or tomorrow you are going to have a rest-day doing the absolute minimum. Then you realise you don't have to keep going for ever, only until the next rest-day which is possibly in a few days time.

In a crisis:

    a). do a bit then rest a bit,
    b). don't get tired,
    c). prioritise,
    d). stop non-coping fantasies.

When wanting a respite from thinking about a crisis (e.g. When I lost my C.F.S./M.E. book data on the computer) get immersed in something different, a TV programme, a hobby or activity.

Talk to someone supportive.

In a crisis, do much less activity to save your energy as a crisis is very exhausting to cope with.

Let yourself fantasize about the best case scenario but gradually get used to the worst possible.

When in a terrible crisis believe a solution is possible. This reduces the pain and helps looking on the bright side.

When in a crisis be kind to yourself.

Having a contingency plan ready can work very well.

When you have had a setback, disappointment or crisis, give yourself time to come to terms with it, and be aware that you may also feel more tired as a result.

Don`t make irrevocable decisions in the middle of a crisis.

Cuddling your partner can help reduce anxiety in a crisis.

When someone is ill in hospital, especially women, they have to keep up appearances, maintain their self-respect and self-esteem, look good and have their own territory marked out with flowers and cards. They have to act alot.

When people come home from hospital they need to re-established their role at home gradually. Allow them to do this.

To empathize with someone takes conscious effort.

If you need to take people up on their offers of help when you are ill, ask them to do small tasks that fit into their routine. They will then be much more likely to offer again.

When ill there's lots of kissing, cuddling and mutual massage possible if sex is out of the question with your partner.

STRESS.

If you've been forced into having a hectic morning, treat yourself to an easier afternoon; or following a hectic day arrange a more relaxed and rewarding one for the next.

Before you start work, decide when you are going to stop for a break.

Irritability is the consequence of fatigue, stress and anxiety. The answer is relaxation alternated with short periods of activity.

When people are tired and irritable, give them space, leave them alone.

Losing some control of events brings some stress, anxiety and non-coping fantasies. The answer is to stop the fantasies and be assertive.

With tiredness come non-coping fantasies. Rest and relaxation replaces these with a refreshing feeling.

Sometimes if I want to reward myself, I lie down, relax and think my favourite thoughts.

Because of the number of routine tasks to do carers can get less pleasurable time to themselves than the sufferers.

Praising and encouraging your partner in all their behaviour at home etc. can lead to them praising and encouraging you; resulting in a double pay-off.

When you are ill all your plans become uncertain and in limbo. Nothing can be decided definitely; visits, holidays, visitors etc.

Dysfunctional beliefs can paralyze you with anxiety.

If you find yourself in a stressful situation; what you must do is recall the times when you were successful in that situation.

Anxiety can come from doing something new or extra to your routine; even thoughts of a holiday. You fear being setback, relapsing, or getting dysfunctional thoughts.

With anxiety can come obsessional and perverse thoughts. These are such that, when you are pleased by something good or beautiful your mind perversely thinks of the direct opposite. This can be disturbing as you worry you might act out this perversity. You wont. Understanding why you are anxious helps combat these obsessional and perverse imaginings.

In getting back to working I have had to overcome anxiety about each stage, from doing a private case at all, doing one a fortnight, then one a week, then organising therapeutic intervention in a case. As my health has improved I have taken on more work, but this has resulted in some feelings of panic and fear of not coping because of the possibility of not having enough energy. Relaxation, defeating dysfunctional beliefs and non-coping fantasies has been very important at each stage.

I wonder how many lives one would have to live to experience all that there is in life.

Being bitter about your affliction only embitters other people against you. You are the loser twice over.
It is more important to know about the person who has the disease than it is to know about the disease the person has. Hypocrates.

174

To maintain a constant appropriate weight only eat when you are hungry.

One can become so obsessed with an activity, be it slimming or making some collection, that one is in danger of losing control; not being able to stop when the time comes; being addicted to the activity. This can then generate fear and anxiety about the obsession.

Taking frequent breaks, at least every hour, extends your overall working time before you get tired.

Be careful that your partner doesn't enjoy the power and control gained by being your carer, so much that they unnecessarily maintain you in your invalidity in order to prolong their position.

After you have been unemployed for some time you have to adapt and fill your time with your own interests. When your health returns and you have to work again, you have to re-adapt and give up working on your own interests in order to work on someone else's and earn a living. This can be irksome. This explains why some people after being unemployed for a long time are relunctant to return to work. They are out of practice and need help to relearn. Ideally you would like to make a living working on your own interests.

If your self-esteem is delicate don't expose yourself to undue criticism.

When you have a chronic illness you can get fed up with being careful and looking after yourself all the time.

If you are trying to work effectively during the week, take the weekend off.

If you cope with life's disappointments magnanimously, new opportunities may come your way. But if you can't cope with your disappointments worse is guaranteed.

175

One can total all the moments of happiness in a day and see if they outnumber the total for pain. Repeat this for a week or year. I wonder if the total happiness in the world outweighs the total pain and sadness.

Angry thoughts can bring aggressive behaviour and bitterness. Don't be angry, be assertive and as a last resort humour can help.

The power of a unpleasant personal remark to cause pain can be very great.

Mary Wesley the novelist started writing at the age of 70. There may be time enough to achieve some of your aims in life.

Rowing with your partner is horrible but making up is nice.

After living and getting used to a certain amount of stress and stimulation, it is often difficult to drop back into a calmer quieter pace of life or even suddenly take on a more demanding life-style.

Don't be afraid of making long range plans and having the determination to stick to them.

Writing a novel or diary about your feelings can have great therapeutic value.

Sensing the fragrance of your wife's perfume and personal scent on her clothes can be very comforting when you are despairing.

Experiencing new fragrances can be pleasing.

Anyone whoever they are, whatever they are can strive for spiritual and personal development.

Chance plays a big role in anyone's life. Denis Healey Labour M.P.

Be resigned to your circumstances but quietly work towards your aims in life. Hinduism.

Be honest with yourself about how you feel.

Getting over-tired can result in you losing your optimism, the power of your reinforcers and pleasures.

Even achieving something small makes you feel happy and dispels depression.

Avoid depending on buying things to make yourself happy.

Be ready to have short-term discomfort for long-term gains.

Every so often you can feel envious of normal people's seemingly endless good health. Don't let yourself be pleased about their illness when it comes. It benefits no-one.

Being depressed seems easily triggered. Sometimes wallowing in the misery is preferable to trying to dispel it. Talk about what upsets you instead of ruminating, can help.

Time does heal most dissatisfactions. Just be patient.

High expectations can lead to disappointments, therefore keep them modest.

Generally be prepared to underfunction when reducing any medication you have been taking.

Sometimes one can be so consumed by one's problem, that it leaves no time to think of anything else.

If and when you suffer a setback in your illness; decide on a little plan of action for your recovery.

In keeping a diary of your illness it is important to be honest with yourself.

As you get older it is vital to keep contact and interested in the younger generation of your family.

Apart from adding interest to your life when you are retired, you never know when you might need them.

After people have suffered a major illness or disaster they often feel motivated to help other people who have suffered the same fate.

When you get a setback, you worry that resting may not restore your former level of health; but it will.

Once you have started thinking and ruminating it is difficult to stop.

We all desire certainty in our lives.

Resting for a special occasion inadvertently can remind you of past aspects of your chronic illness.

A little walk well within your limits everyday can be a real tonic.

If you have a problem preying on your mind, take a mental rest from thinking about it. Don't presuppose the worst.

With chronic illness you can't help but learn about yourself.

You do feel less charitable when you feel hard pressed or attacked. (Like when the Government's budget is aimed at cutting your benefit).

I feel everyone should have the opportunity during their life to spend some time being creative. In writing, whilst convalescing, I have discovered a source of great pleasure, which I would be sorry to lose.

Unexpected empathy from an unlikely person can be very moving.

Each day don't always work up to your limit; leave some time and energy for coping with the unexpected.

Often your fears and anxieties come to you when you have stopped an activity and are physically and mentally relaxing.

Great happiness is sometimes juxtaposed with great sadness; like the man who said his greatest joy was when all of his family survived after his house burnt down.

When you are acutely ill, you remember all the past occasions when you were poorly.

When you have been upset, it takes the passage of time to restore your feelings to normal.

When you are chronically ill, you cannot better yourself by working hard, or great endeavour. You have to be more patient and do what you can in a sustainable way.

When you are chronically ill and poor, you and your family feel outside the mainstream of society; can't afford the cinema, theatre, holidays etc. It really is worst when holiday programmes on TV show what other people can afford.

When you are depressed it is as though you are supersensitive to all the world's pain.

Even with a chronic illness, having a plan of activity for the day, no matter how limited, is very reassuring and comforting. You know what you are going to do and can look forward to it.

When you are feeling low, think of all the people who love you and of good memories. This can give you a warm reassuring feeling.

When you are ill and have psychological symptoms you need much empathic discussion to help understand what is happening. Doctors rarely have time to provide this.

Having a chronic illness could result in you occupying the centre of the family gaining much attention. Others in the family could resent this and feel neglected.

With a chronic illness, the psychological damage caused by an unsympathetic partner or family could be horrendous.

The experience of C.F.S./M.E. I have gained as a sufferer has taught me what my partner needs when she is ill and I am the carer. I didn't realise how useful such knowledge would be.

Psychological illness is probably far worse than just physical sickness.

Frustrated plans produce a depressed mood and aggression.

If you can see the humorous side of your illness, so much the better.

Fear is diminished by familiarity. Bertrand Russell.

To ward off a melancholy mood alternate your activities. A short walk well within your capabilities can be beautiful.

When ill you should be allowed to make the best of it; to enjoy yourself; to plan as nice a day as far as possible.

When you are feeling well, reassure your family that you still love and care for them inspite of your illness.

If you are worried by people asking you to do things - say no.

Give yourself time to get used to a new idea or situation. You will accommodate.

Walking is the balm of the mind.

Don't have a strict timetable for your work. It is frustrating and punishing when you fail to keep to it and it creates pressure to keep up. Have a plan by all means but not a timetable.

Aim to always feel nice and comfortable whether working or resting.

The worst part about being seriously ill is not understanding what is happening to you; not being able to predict the course of a recovery; not being able to see an end to it.

No-one suspects your motivation to get back to health when you have a broken leg but when psychological symptoms occur even with a physical illness, they do. The subtle accusation of malingering is soon apparent.

When helping people who are ill, do things the way they would like, not the way you would like.

I really know, after being chronically ill, what the saying "every cloud has a silver lining" means. Every setback or misfortune can have some advantages.

Even chronically ill people need some colour and excitement in their lives. Try to make some.

When you are really ill or exhausted, you need to be left alone, given space to recover. If this happens to your partner they may become less talkative, less responsive to you. Do not blame yourself. It is nothing you have done. It is not your fault.

Emotional reunions are fatiguing. Take account of this.

You can enjoy your mental life nearly as much as your physical life.

Chronic illness is alright as long as you don't struggle (like inside a straight jacket) for something better, too soon; don't be impatience.

JONI'S STORY.

Probably the worst chronic condition is quadraplegia and depression. However, even this has been overcome by some people. What follows is the story of Joni Eareckson's fight against just these conditions.

She broke her neck in a diving accident in July 1967 resulting in being paralyzed from the neck down. She felt compelled to share her incredible adventure because of what she has learned.

What she has to say is relevant to sufferers of chronic illness in general and those with C.F.S./M.E. in particular. Her insights are in italic print.

After the accident doctors did not tell her what was happening to her; they did not explain the physiology of the damage she'd incurred. (With C.F.S./M.E. you struggle to understand what is happening to you through the course of the illness).

You need doctors to explain clearly what they are going to do to you and the likely effects of the treatment. There is much fear.

Friendship with others with the same illness is very comforting.

Your illness causes pain to your relatives and friends.

Relive good memories to take your mind off the physical and psychological pain.

Chronic illness can produce much spiritual progress in you although you probably don't appreciate it at the time.

No matter what has happened to you, trust in God.

Try to reward your visitors by being pleasant and avoiding bitterness, to help ensure they come again.

The toughest part of the battle against chronic illness is the psychological aspect.

At times you will feel suicidal. Everyone in this position feels this.

Find someone to whom you can honestly talk to about how terrible you really feel.

Don't develop false beliefs about your illness. They will let you down and disappoint you in the end although they may serve to let you down gently and to come to terms with your illness in the short term.

Joni felt her accident was part of God's plan for her. (However, I believe God is a great companion, that he does not plan to inflict misfortune on people, but that the universe follows its own course and in so doing both good and tragic things can happen. But God can help you cope and comfort you).

Joni continues:
Chronic illness and the consequent confinement result in suffering sensory deprivation. This heightens the sense of loss at sudden changes in your life, resulting from your illness. Loss can lead to depression. You mourn the loss of all the normal possibilities in life for you.

Have faith, hope and trust in God.

In hospital there are caring nurses and unpleasant ones.

God; either He exist or He doesn't.

We all want to see our life have purpose and meaning.

Seeing the progress in people with the same illness as you is comforting.

Being creative, in writing, cooking or painting when chronically ill can give renewed hope.

Before my accident I didn't need Christ. Now I need Him desperately.

When chronically ill you need a plan of action which provides small goals to look forward to. Achievement of small accomplishments can make you feel proud and exhilarated and this generates optimism.

No matter how ill you are, list your potential abilities.

Envying people who are well is common but painful.

Chronic illness can give rise to feelings of hopelessness and worthlessness.

Life-after-death means that you will not be trapped in a useless body for ever. From the standpoint of eternity my body is only a flicker in the time-span of forever.

(This applies to anyone who is chronically ill).

Chronic illness can make you become selfish; be careful of this pitfall.

Taking part in the world is a refreshing and stimulating experience - especially in giving talks to interested groups about your condition.

Confidence increases as you make new achievements.

We are not always responsible for the circumstances in which we find ourselves. However we are responsible for the way we respond to them.
Joni still paralyzed, says at the end of her book,

"I was at a point in my life where I was actually satisfied with my situation."

Since being paralyzed I have learned to work as a counsellor to other young people, learned to write, draw and paint using my mouth and mastered the art of public speaking.

(In doing this, Joni created a social life for herself regardless of her handicap. Even with C.F.S./M.E. and the chronic lack of energy it is possible to have a variety of people come to visit you at home just for a ten minute chat or to talk to on the telephone.

Don't be shy about assertively inviting friends to see you. They often are just waiting to be asked).

Joni continues:
I achieved complete emotional independence through complete dependence on God.

The only thing we can take to heaven with us is our character. (This applies equally to C.F.S./M.E. sufferers. Make it a goal in life to develop as good a character as possible).

At the end of her book Joni was asked if she was happy and she said *"I really am. I wouldn't change my life for anything. I even feel privileged."*

Wisdom is trusting God, not asking, "why God?"

Eareckson, J. (1979). Joni. The unforgettable story of a young woman`s struggle against quadriplegia and depression. London: Pickering & Inglis.

CHAPTER 4. CHRISTIAN PRINCIPLES.

I ASKED GOD.

I asked God for strength that I might achieve,
I was made weak to humbly obey,
I asked for health, that I might do greater things,
I was given infirmity that I might do better things,
I asked for riches, that I might be happy,
I was given poverty that I might be wise,
I asked for power that I might have the praise of
    men,
I was given weakness that I might feel the need of
    God,
I asked for all things that I might enjoy life,
I was given life, that I might enjoy all things,
I got nothing that I asked for but everything I had
    hoped for. Almost despite myself, my unspoken
    prayers were answered.
I am among all men most richly blessed.

Author unknown.

Truth will always prevail because God is truth.

Some find that belief in a personal God helpful.

God is with you. Each improvement is an indication
of His presence saying "hang on".

It may be that good health is a glimpse into the
Kingdom of Heaven.

"Death is nothing at all, .. I have only slipped
away into the next room. I am I and you are you.
Whatever we were to each other that we are still.
Call me by my old familiar name, speak to me in the
easy way which you always used. Put no difference
into your tone; wear no forced air of solemnity or
sorrow. Laugh as we always laughed at the little
jokes we enjoyed together. Play, smile, think of
me, pray for me. Let my name be ever the household
word that it always was. Let it be spoken without
effect, without the ghost of a shadow on it. Life
means all that it ever meant. It is the same as it

ever was; there is absolutely unbroken continuity. What is this death but a negligible accident? Why should I be out of mind because I am out of sight? I am but waiting for you, for an interval, somewhere very near just around the
corner.. All is well."
Letter From Canon Henry Scott Holland (1847-1918) On Death.

The greatest worry in life must be about death and Canon Holland smooths away its suffering leaving us with the feeling that all of our other worries are diminished.

A man walking in the snow sees his own and another pair of footprints. Asking whose they are, God says they are His."I am always with you." He says."But why, when I am really down do I see only one pair of footprints, why do you leave me?" says the man. "That`s when I carry you." says God.

Do not be afraid, for I have redeemed you. I have called you by your name; you are mine. When you walk through the waters, I'll be with you. You will never sink beneath the waves.

Do not be afraid, for I have redeemed you. I have called you by your name; you are mine. When the fire is burning all around you, you will never be consumed by the flames.

Do not be afraid, for I have redeemed you. I have called you by your name; you are mine. When the fear of loneliness is looming, then remember I am at your side.

Do not be afraid, for I have redeemed you. I have called you by your name; you are mine. When you dwell in the exile of the stranger, remember you are precious in my eyes.

Do not be afraid, for I have redeemed you. I have called you by your name; you are mine.

You are mine, 0 my child, I am your Father, and I

love you with a perfect love.

Do not be afraid, for I have redeemed you. I have called you by your name; you are mine.
Gerard Markland (b. 1953). based on Isaiah 43:1-4 @ 1978
Kevin Mayhew Ltd.

Chronic illness can be very lonely but these quotations help you believe that God is an ever-present ally.

The Lord is my light and my salvation; whom shall I fear? The Lord is the strength of my life; of whom shall I be afraid? Bible, Psalm 27.

No-one is alone in their suffering. That is what Christ on the cross means.

Thank God for giving you your positive feelings and strength of spirit.

God so loved the world, that he gave his only begotten Son, that whosoever believeth in him should not perish, but have everlasting life.
Bible., John 3:16.

Verily, verily, I say unto you, He that believeth on me hath everlasting life.
Bible., John 6:47.

"Most gladly therefore will I rather glory in my infirmities that the power of Christ may rest upon me for when I am weak then I am strong".
Bible, 2 Corinthians 12, 9.

"He that overcometh shall inherit all things and I will be his God and he shall be my son".
Bible, Revelations 21.1-7.

See, I have refined you, though not as silver; I have tested you in the furnace of affliction.
Bible, Isaiah 48:10.

Pray that God will give you the strength to cope with C.F.S./M.E.

Think of our personal God. God loves you. Think "love will get me through this illness".

The God of the universe is with you; he is on your side; be joyful.

"Beloved, let us love one another; for love is of God and everyone that loveth is born of God and knoweth God. He that loveth not, knoweth not God for God is love."
Bible, 1 John, 4, 7, 8.

Heaven. "Eye hath not seen, nor ear heard neither have entered into the heart of man, the things which God hath prepared for them that love Him."
Bible, 1. Corinthians, 2, 9.

Remember that the Gideon Bible has a list of passages that can help you in different circumstances.

Christ said "He that hath my commandments and keepeth them, he it is that loveth me: and he that loveth me shall be loved of my Father and I will love him and will manifest myself to him".
Bible, John, 14, 21-22.

The power of the Lord is with you. God is in your very thoughts, helping to make them pleasant and rewarding.

God chose you to live.

Sometimes God speaks to you, for instance through music or friendship or some recovery or a robin on the windowsill. Be sure not to miss Him.

For I reckon that the sufferings of this present time are not worthy to be compared with the glory which shall be revealed in us.
Bible, Romans, 8, 18.

Look for the signs of hope that God gives you.

Jesus said unto him "If thou canst believe, all things are possible to him that believeth."
Bible, St. Mark 9, 23.

Ponder anew what the Almighty can do, if to the end He befriend thee. Hymn, Praise to the Lord, the Almighty, the King of creation. By Joachim Neander (1650-1680)

God is the light that illuminates our consciousness.

Yea, though I walk through the valley of the shadow of death, I will fear no evil, for thou art with me.
Bible, Psalm 23, 4.

Love is patient; love is kind and envies no-one. Love is never boastful, nor conceited, nor rude; never selfish, not quick to take offence. Love keeps no score of wrongs; does not gloat over other men's sins, but delights in the truth. There is nothing love cannot face; there is no limit to its faith and its endurance.
Bible, 1, Corinthians, 13, 4-7.

How blest are those who hunger and thirst to see right prevail. They shall be satisfied.
Bible, Matthew, 5, 6.

Jesus said "And be assured, I am with you always, to the end of time".
Bible, Matthew, 28, 20.

Remember the best is yet to come.
Gordon A. Hendry.

Death is not extinguishing the light, it is only putting out the lamp because the dawn has come.
Rabindranath Tagore.

Life is only for love.   Time is only that we may find God.

St Bernard of Clairvieux, Abbot of the Cistercian Foundation of Clairvieux in France in the twelfth century.

Christian joy is all pervading and it brings with it a wonderful sense of security and freedom from anxiety, the like of which one has never known before.   Jesus refers to this wonderful transformation in our lives as the second birth - being born again. We know for certain that the Creator of the universe and of life itself, through all eternity, is listening with love and responding to our every prayer, no matter how trivial that prayer may be. We see and hear God in everyone we meet and indeed, in every manifestation of life.

From "The Best is Yet to Come, a personal philosophy", by G.A.Hendry 1991.

I said to the man who stood at the gate of the year: "Give me a light that I may tread safely into the unknown." And he replied, "Go out into the darkness and put your hand into the hand of God. That shall be to you better than light and safer than a known way".

M.Louise Haskins.

Don't worry over anything whatever; tell God every detail of your needs in earnest and thankful prayer, and the peace of God, which transcends human understanding, will keep constant guard over your hearts and minds as they rest in Christ Jesus.

Bible, Philippians, 4, 6-7.

Jesus said: "And so I tell you, ask and it will be given you, search and you will find, knock and the door will be opened to you. The one who asks will always receive; the one who is searching will always find and the door opened to the man who knocks".

Luke 11, 9-10.

Your ultimate destination is to desire unity with God, and when you have achieved that, you've *achieved everything; And unless you've achieved that, you`ve achieved nothing.*

Lord Hailsham.

Be comforted, he who seeks God, has already found Him.

Blaise Pascal.

Jesus said: "I tell you this: anything you did for one of my brothers here, however humble, you did for me".

Bible, Matthew, 25, 40.

Blessed are the merciful: for they shall obtain mercy.
Blessed are the pure in heart: for they shall see God.
Blessed are the peacemakers: for they shall be called the children of God.

Bible, Matthew, 5, 1-13.

Come unto me, all ye that labour and are heavy laden, and I will refresh you.

Bible, Matthew, 11, 28-29.

May the peace of God which passes all understanding be with you now and for ever more.

Blessing. The Order of Holy Communion Rite B.

Going to church and singing the beautiful words and sentiments can greatly improve a low mood.

Recompense to no man evil for evil. Provide things honest in the sight of all men. If it be possible as much as lieth in you, live peaceably with all men. Dearly beloved, avenge not yourselves, but rather give place unto wrath: for it is written, Vengeance is mine; I will repay saith the Lord.
Therefore if thine enemy hunger, feed him; if he thirst, give him drink: for in so doing thou shalt heap coals of fire on his head. Be not overcome of evil, but over-come evil with good.

Bible, Romans, 12, 17-21.

God wants us to be loving and caring with everyone.

O my God you have surpassed all my expectations and I will sing your mercies for evermore".
Basilique de St.Therese. Lisieux. France.

"I believe in the sun even when it does not shine, I believe in love even if I do not feel it, I believe in God even if I do not see him".
Young Jew.

"And I saw a new earth: for the first heaven and the first earth were passed away and there was no more sea. And God shall wipe away all tears from their eyes; and there shall be no more death, neither sorrow , nor crying, neither shall there be any more pain: for the former things are passed away."
Bible, Revelations, 21, 1 and 4.

Feeling well is the greatest gift from God.

It's your spiritual development that matters more than anything else in life.

In trying to be a Christian you get the freedom to enjoy people without making dangerous liaisons, value their achievement without being envious and get the pleasure of their possessions without coverting them.

Being a Christian is affording people their achievements when they deserve it.

Being a Christian is about not hurting people even though you have the power.

Paradise on earth will come for you when you embrace the love of God. He is on your side, always with you - feeling your joy and your pain.

If you don't finish all you want to do before you die, you can finish it in heaven.

Having C.F.S./M.E. you may not be able to do much, but look for little ways in which you can assist God`s creation.

"And now, my friends, all that is true, all that is noble, all that is just and pure, all that is lovable and gracious, whatever is excellent and admirable - fill all your thoughts with these things".
Bible, Philippians, 4, 8.

"I see life as a progression towards God - an increase of love".
Leo Tolstoy. Russian author of the book "War and Peace"

"I believe that the meaning of the life of every man is to be found only in increasing the love that is in him, that this increase of love leads man, even in this life, to ever greater and greater blessedness".
Leo Tolstoy.

Love thy neighbour as thyself.
The Summary of The Law. The Order for Holy Communion. Rite B, from The Alternative Service Book 1980.

In the worst of times God sends little compensations. Look out for them.

When I was really ill and contemplating suicide, fear of the repercussions in the after-life was the uppermost thought.

Jesus said, "Do not let your hearts be troubled. Trust in God; trust also in me. In my Father's house are many rooms; if it were not so, I would have told you. I am going there to prepare a place for you. And if I go and prepare a place for you, I will come back and take you to be with me that you also may be where I am".
Bible, John 14, 1-3.

I have had many religious dreams of Christ and cathedrals, many dreams of people coming to see me. If God wanted to communicate with you how would He do it in a way that could be proved? Did God communicate with me or were they just dreams? Whichever it was I was helped by them.

And we most humbly beseech thee of thy goodness O Lord to comfort and succour all those who in this transitory life are in trouble, sorrow, need, sickness or any other adversity.
Order of Holy Communion, Rite B, First Intercession.

I am not sure that God knows what the future will be.

Death marks the beginning of a great adventure experiencing all of God's creation preserved for us in heaven.
John Polkinghorne, President of Queen's College, Cambridge.

Getting old and more infirm maybe is a mechanism for making death and the potential for life thereafter more attractive.

With God, anything is possible.
Ranulph Fiennes.

Here for a season, then above,
O lamb of God, I come. Hymn: Just as I am. By Charlotte Elliott (1789-1871).

If you are in doubt about making a particular decision, the right course of action may not be immediately obvious. Therefore ask 'what would love do? what would Christ do?'

Forgiveness should come after repentance as in the Christian faith, rather than before.

Forgiving people who have hurt you must be done eventually and when achieved is a release and relief.

Our birth is but a sleep and a forgetting;
The Soul that rises with us, our life's star
Hath had elsewhere its setting
And cometh from afar.

Wordsworth.   Ode on Intimations of Immortality,   from Recollections of Early Childhood.

In this life, we are not material beings on a
spiritual journey, but we are spiritual beings on a
material journey. For whatsoever a man soweth, that
shall he reap.

Bible. Galatians 6:7.

Great modern-day scientists are asking whether there
is a purpose in the universe or not? Is there a God?
Is there life after death? They believe that the
universe has a story and development, from a
beginning in a huge explosion - the Big Bang. They
think there is a genuine openness to the future and
that God is accompanying its development with
sympathy and understanding. He is the great
companion - the fellow sufferer who understands.
Some scientists are saying that the universe is so
constructed that it knew that Man was coming and that
life after death or resurrection is a real
possibility. Science and the Christian religion are
moving closer to each other as never before.

(Tilby, A. (1992). Soul. An Introduction to the New Cosmology, - Time, Consciousness and God. London: BBC Education.

A STRANGE DREAM – OR – A MESSAGE FROM HEAVEN?
Since the deaths of my father-in-law, and a dear lady, a friend at St. Chad's Church, I have wondered whether either of them might send a message indicating that they are alright, as I've read can happen with people bereaved. As time passed and nothing happened I began to give up; but when the dream occurred in the night of Tuesday 14 February 2006 it was half expected.

It was a dream but very much revelatory; nothing like I have ever experienced before. It was stunning; earth-shattering in impact;

not confused like dreams often can be. I was lying down in heaven surrounded by people eating. I thought at first they were eating me, but on reflection they could not have been as I was not being diminished or consumed.

In the distance there was an extremely bright light, like the sun but it not only shone with light, but also love, happiness and comfort. I felt such extreme joy I could scarcely cope with it.

There was laughter and gaiety, but when people spoke, I heard them in my mind.

Then first the still image of my friend appeared then that of my father-in-law. I was told, that they were O.K. How is this possible; why is this possible, I queried. The answer came that it is one's good deeds in life (doing something for other people) that are rewarded in heaven more than a thousand fold, whilst misdeeds and crimes in life have a double disadvantage. First of all they are a waste of precious time that could have been used for good in life and secondly, they are not rewarded again in heaven, as are good deeds. Both my friend and my father-in-law were now enjoying the fruits of what they had sown in life. They were now enjoying the treasures in heaven that they had amassed during in their lifetime, came the sure logical explanation.

I was aware of souls floating in the dimming light, darkness and cold stretching out a long way behind me. These were not happy but reflecting on where they had placed themselves in relation to God in the after-life by their crimes and misdeeds in life. The worse the crimes and unrepentance, the further out in the pitch black they were. This was a hell of their own creation. Again this was a clear insight and felt immediately in mind. No one spoke.

I was told to pass on messages to my father, mother and brother, (who do have religious beliefs but do not attend church regularly,) because each have done so much for others, through their teaching careers and for my mother, through her selfless devotion to raising her family, that none of them should worry about their place in heaven when their time comes. This was very strongly felt and so too was the responsibility for passing on these messages.

At one point the people around me were pondering how to motivate young men to take a full part in life and my mother who was there surprisingly, created a surge of happy emotion and hilarity when she suggested they be encouraged to make babies.

The pleasure felt through out the dream was so extreme it was bordering on pain and as I emerged into consciousness I found myself crying. My wife beside me in bed, shook me and asked if I was alright. My tears were of joy not anguish; it was an overwhelming joy that told of every little kindness we give to others, contributing and weighed in the balance, at the end of our lives. It was reminiscent of the story of the 'widow's mite' in the bible. It was a very small amount and all that she could afford to give, but it counted even so.

I was left in no doubt that life is a preparation for death and the after-life. I could now readily recognise people around me and in the news who were wasting their lives on wholly selfish endeavours or worse, that generated nothing of value for eternity. I learned that it is not money or the acquisition of it that is wrong but what one does with it. The rich are in danger, as with wealth comes the responsibility to do something with it that is beneficial to others. I understood in an instant that the only treasures we take to heaven are our deeds and the character we have built for ourselves.

At the end of my dream I knew I had been allowed a glimpse into the here-after and afforded a great privilege indeed. I am only an ordinary person, so why have I been so honoured?

"Why? Because you looked, because you sought after this knowledge; because you inquired.", came the answer. That was the reason.

Continually I felt intense joy throughout the dream; so intense it was beyond comprehension. The Light of God was ever present bathing the joy with a warm love of protection and belonging. I now understood that the spread of the Gospel by the disciples and St. Paul in particular, was undertaken because of a huge irresistible urge they had to tell others, everyone, this wonderful truth that God exists; that life beyond death exists. The similarity between my dream and biblical stories is apparent and shows that such experiences are possible even now for ordinary people.

A profound realisation has occurred to me; if God responded to my concerns with this dream visitation, then He did hear me. God does follow one's every thought and knows one's every need.

In fact the two people outside my family, I have told about this dream, both described having similar experiences following bereavement. It was my mother who suggested I put this story in the parish magazine. It would be interesting to hear from anyone else who has a similar tale to tell. **Recently I met an acquaintance, a Muslim woman of Asian descent, and told her my story. She too replied that she had had two similar dreams following bereavement.**

This dream has been life-changing for me. It is a marvellous revelation; something I've sought for a long time. And now I am certain of the answer.

I now understand my life better. Illness closed one path through life and resulted in following another. It seems to be saying that whatever happens to you, good or ill, learn from the experiences because all of them can lead to opportunities to do good and build your own character.

This new certainty allows you to wake each morning, fresh in the knowledge of God's creative genius in designing the universe and one's part in it. The more complete science becomes – the greater the wonder.

It is true: "The greatest thing you'll ever learn is just to love, and be loved in return". From the film Moulin Rouge.

R. Paul Gregory.
Published in St. Chad's Church Magazine June 2006

MEDJUGORJE.
The book by Fr. Ren, Laurentin and professor Henri Joyeux (1987) Scientific & Medical Studies on the Apparitions At Medjugorje. Dublin: Veritas Publications, said that on 24th June 1981 four girls and two boys aged between 10 and 16 years in the village of Byakovici in Medjugorje, in the former Yugoslavia, as a group started to see apparitions of what they said was the Virgin Mary. These apparitions were such that no-one but the six young people could see them. They spoke to the apparition and she spoke to them. This continued every day at first, then weekly and monthly up to the present time. They are still happening now.

The six young people, who as a group, saw the Virgin on the second day, were those who then continued to receive daily apparitions. Four of them – Marija, Vicka, Ivan and Jakov – have seen the Virgin virtually daily, with occasional interruptions, since then up to 1990; while the two others – Mirjana and Ivanka – have seen the Virgin only once a year since their daily apparitions ended some years ago.

The claims of these young people have been medically and scientifically investigated to an intensity never before possible with a supernatural event. The apparitions could not be proved to be fraudulent. The simplest explanation was that the students were talking with the Virgin Mary. The messages given to them by Mary have been recorded and have caused an estimated 12 million people to visit Medjugorje on pilgrimages.

In a second book by Dudley Plunkett the actual messages are described. (Plunkett,D. 1990. Queen of Prophets. The Spiritual

Message of Medjugorje. London: Darton, Longman and Todd. The most powerful and astonishing thing she has said is

"I have come to tell the world that God is truth: He exists. In Him is true good fortune and fullness of life".

These words have been a revelation and huge comfort to me through the worst periods of my illness. They are recorded here in the hope that they will bring to you the same salvation as they have me.

More imformation about this phenomenon can be found by putting the word "Medjugorje" into the search engine www.google.co.uk
www.medjugorje.org is the main website. Make a visit today; it will change your life.

* * *

"The resurrection of Jesus Christ speaks of a destiny for all matter as well as humanity - that is all creation",
Dr. J Polkinghorne of Queens` College Cambridge.

He believes that the pattern of human beings which dissolves at death is remembered by God and will be recreated by Him in some unimaginable new environment of his choosing. It has happened to Jesus Christ.

APPARITION OF THE VIRGIN MARY AT ZEITUN, EGYPT
1968

If any more evidence of the existence of God were needed, read the following account available on a website. Insert "Zeitun" into www.google.co.uk

"Official investigations have been carried out with the result that it has been considered an undeniable fact that the Blessed Virgin

Mary has been appearing on Zeitun Church in a clear and bright luminous body seen by all present in front of the church, whether Christian or Moslem"

Report of General Information and Complaints Department, Zeitun, Egypt 1968.

While all in America were watching the the Chicago riots at the Democratic Convention, or viewing live war zone broadcasts from Vietnam or were being mesmerized by the Watergate hearings on television, the Mother of God was appearing for tens of thousands to see in the land of the pyramids at a Coptic church constructed to commemorate the area in Egypt where she had come with Joseph and Jesus when they all fled from Herod. Starting in April, 1968, her apparitions of light changed the lives of thousands. Her appearances at Zeitun were astounding. She was seen by more than a million people. The apparitions were broadcast by Egyptian TV, photographed by hundreds of professional photographers and personally witnessed by Egyptian President Abdul Nasser, an avowed Marxist. The apparitions lasted for three years with numerous unaccountable healings recorded by various medical professionals. The local police, who initially thought the apparitions were an elaborate hoax, searched a 15-mile radius surrounding the site to uncover any type of device that could be used to project such images. They were completely unsuccessful.

Moslems who saw the apparitions chanted from the Koran, *"Mary, God has chosen thee. And purified thee; He has chosen thee. Above all women."* She was seen accompanied by doves of light in apparitions that lasted from a few minutes to as long as nine hours. Kyrillos VI, the Orthodox patriarch, formed a commission to investigate the apparitions. A number of the commissioners observed plumes of fragrant purple smoke rising from the church at the time of the apparitions and the figure of a woman surrounded by a very bright globe of light accompanied by doves of light. A digitally-enhanced, negative image of one television frame is shown at the top of this page to enable you to see an outline of what was seen by hundreds of thousands in Egypt.

While the appearances at Zeitun were silent, the silence spoke volumes to those who came to see and strengthen their faith. The local Coptic Patriarch, **Kyrillos VI, publicly announced a year after the apparitions started that he had no doubt that the Mother of God was appearing above the roof of St. Mary's Coptic Church.**

For those who, like Thomas, needed to see for themselves, Mary offered an unequivocal televised demonstration at Zeitun. Yet, because of an unresponsive media and an indifferent world, very few outside of Egypt learned of her astonishing appearances there until well after they had ended.

More recently, the appearance of a woman clothed in light has been observed above the roof of the Church of St. Damian in Shoubra, Egypt, a suburb of Cairo. Starting in 1983 and seen with increasing frequency in the mid-1980's, the woman was seen by thousands walking above the church bathed in light in apparitions lasting up to five hours. Shenouda III, the head of the Coptic Church at the time, established a commission to investigate the beautiful lady of light. In 1987, the commission concluded:

`"Let us thank the Lord for this blessing on the people of Egypt and for the repetition of this phenomenon. We should also like to thank the police`

and the Department of the Interior for their untiring
efforts at maintaining safety and good order among
the thousands of people who have spent day and night
at prayer. We ask all the people to remain calm. Thus
they may worthily receive the blessing of the Virgin,
of St. Damian and of all the saints. May God save our
country. We pray that he may guide Egypt and all her
children to every success. May this phenomenon be a
pledge of well-being for them and for all nations."

As in Zeitun, the silent witness of the Mother of God renewed the faith of tens of thousands and brought both Moslem and Christian to a place of peace where all could pray to the God who loved them enough to remind them of his love by sending His Mother.

GHOSTS OF THE TSUNAMI.
Reprinted from the Daily Mail, Thursday, December 28, 2006. By Colin Wilson, author and expert on the paranormal.

Spectres on the beach. Voices calling from empty buildings. On the second anniversary of the tsunami, the extraordinary story of how one British couple set out to bring peace to the victims' spirits.

Half an hour before the tsunami struck Phi Phi island, the sea retreated two miles, making it look as if someone had pulled an enormous bathplug. Locals who had been taught about tsunamis knew what this meant, and many lost no time retreating to higher ground - the island is a plain between two mountains.

But the majority of people on the beaches were foreign tourists, escaping from the winter at home, and they stayed to gaze in astonishment at the mudscape that had opened up before them. Ten minutes later, a 25-foot wave struck at 100mph, sweeping away buildings, trees and cars.

What was left on the plain looked like Hiroshima after the nuclear bomb. Bodies were washed up on the beaches for weeks afterwards, and the smell of decaying flesh and rotten fish was everywhere. In all, at least 200,000 people had been killed across the region.

For the first four days after the catastrophe on Boxing Day, 2004, everyone on Phi Phi island was too stunned to do anything but clear up the giant piles of debris, seaweed and corpses, and try to help the survivors.

It was just as they were starting to regain some sense of normality that the reports of ghosts began. There were tales of half-naked people seen wandering among wrecked buildings, of voices calling in distress from empty beaches, of a spectral woman seen walking along the shoreline at night, crying out for her child.

'My staff are getting really panicked,' said Chaiyun Trisuwan, general manager of the Phi Phi Island Village resort, which was used as a temporary mortuary for corpses from a neighbouring bay. 'There are rumours - some guy saw this, some guy saw that. This is definitely the number one problem.'

Trisuwan's workers became so unnerved that he had to hire security guards to accompany them home after dark. Meanwhile, in Patong, on nearby Phuket Island, another security guard quit his job after hearing a woman's voice crying 'Help me!' all night from a badly damaged and utterly deserted hotel.

On one beach, volunteer searchers who went to investigate sounds of laughter and singing found only an expanse of bare sand. A family in Khao Lak complained that their telephone rang day and night, and that when they answered it, they heard voices of dead friends and relatives begging for help.

Taxi drivers even claimed they had picked up phantom passengers. BBC news correspondent Tony Cheng interviewed the driver of a tuk-tuk minivan named Lek, who recounted how he picked up seven foreign tourists late on the night of January 6, a week and a half after the disaster.

'Go to Kata Beach,' the tourists told him, after agreeing a 200 baht fare. Lek drove for a short distance, but then felt numb all over his body. Looking around, he saw the cab was empty.

Lek told Tony Cheng: 'I am going to get a new job. I have a daughter to support, but I'm too scared to go out driving at night'.

Other drivers spoke of a colleague who had picked up a foreign man and his Thai girl friend who asked to go to the airport. After a while, the driver glanced into the rear-view mirror and found an empty seat behind him.

A Thai psychologist, Piyamanutham Wallop, declared that all these strange reports were simply the result of post traumatic stress disorder.   Another doctor insisted that it was mass hallucination due to the fact that Thais are very superstitious.

Most Thais themselves had a different explanation. They believe that the spirits of the dead need to be laid to rest by relatives, and that when this is not done their ghosts remain trapped on earth, unable to escape.

According to the Thais, the ghosts of people who have died a sudden or violent death face particular problems. Like the traumatised survivors of a car accident, they wander around in a state of total confusion. They need help before they can leave life behind.

That, according to local people, is why so few of the tsunami ghost sightings were of native Thais. They had already received the help they needed to move on, from Buddhist priests and relatives, while the westerners did not realise what had happened to them and were lingering behind.

Strange as it may seem, this view would now be endorsed by most western experts on parapsychology. They too have come to believe that ghosts are usually dead people who do not know they are dead and thus become stuck in earthbound reality.

When I, Colin Wilson the author, heard the accounts of the tsunami ghosts, it seemed obvious to me that this was what had happened to them.

At first, conscious of the feelings of those who lost loved ones in the disaster, I was reluctant to write about the subject – but then I discovered some astonishing work that had been done to bring peace to these restless spirits.

I now believe that this whole story offers inspiring proof of the reality of the afterlife and the way in which the dead can be helped by the living. To understand it fully, we need to begin not in Thailand but in Britain.

The key to the modern understanding of ghosts was an observation made by an obstetric surgeon in a London maternity hospital. Her name was Florence Barrett, and she was the wife of Sir William Barrett, a professor of physics. On the evening of January 12, 1924, she came home with a strange story to tell.

One of her patients had suffered a heart attack after giving birth, and as Lady Barrett held her hand, the woman said: 'Don't let it get dark - it's getting darker and darker.'
Then she looked across the room and said: 'Oh, lovely, lovely! '
'What's lovely?'
'Lovely brightness, wonderful beings,' said the woman. 'Why, it's father. He's so glad I'm coming.' Then she started with surprise. 'There's Vida!'

Vida was the patient's younger sister, who had died two weeks earlier, but the woman had not been told in case it upset her. She died an hour later, continuing to hold a normal conversation with the people around her bed but still seeing her dead father and sister and the 'lovely light'.

Sir William Barrett was so fascinated by this incident that he began making enquiries in hospitals, and soon found that most doctors and nurses could tell similar stories. He went on to write a book about it called 'Death Bed Visions'.

In the 1940s, one of his admirers, a Latvian researcher named Dr Karlis Osis, had the sensible idea of sending out a questionnaire to hundreds of other doctors and nurses asking for their observations on dying patients. He learned that a huge percentage saw dead relatives. Dying children often saw angels, and were puzzled to discover that they had no wings.

Another researcher, Erlendur Haraldsson, went to India to find out whether people from a different culture would have the same kind of deathbed experiences.

The answer was an emphatic 'yes' - and in the 1960s, a third researcher, Professor Douglas Dean, discovered that this holds true across people of all religions: Muslims, Jews, Buddhists, even Aborigines. In other words, it seems that a vast percentage of people who die quietly in their beds are guided from this world to 'the next' - whatever that may be, by the spirits of people they have loved or been close to.

But for people who die violently, or under strange circumstances, it seems things can be more difficult, and in their confusion they become 'earth bound', unaware of where to go next.

These ghosts are then dependent on the help of the living - priests, relatives, or (as we shall see) psychic investigators - to convince them of their plight, and to show them how to leave life behind.

The classic book on the subject is by a Chicago doctor, Carl Wickland, and is called 'Fifty Years Among the Dead'. Wickland begins by explaining how, when he was a medical student, he married a nurse who was psychic.

One day when he came home after dissecting a corpse, he found his wife feeling dizzy. Suddenly, a masculine voice spoke from her mouth: 'Why are you cutting my leg?'

Since Wickland had just been dissecting the corpse's leg, he realised that the voice must belong to its owner. It seemed the ghost had followed him back from the hospital - and because this individual had died suddenly, he had no idea he was dead.

It took a lot of argument, to persuade the ghost that, since his body was now in the dissecting room, he must really be dead, and to send him off in search of the 'lovely light'.

This light seems to be a kind of portal between this world and the next, and Wickland came to realise that in the confusion of sudden death, it is easy to miss. The dead person goes on living in a kind of bad dream from which it is impossible to wake up, and has to be encouraged to see the portal.

Wickland's discoveries caused a revolution among psychical researchers, and led to the formation of dozens of 'rescue' circles. These all used the same methods Wickland had pioneered: that is, they talked to earthbound spirits, and tried to convince them they were dead.

Sometimes, spirits who had already been rescued joined in and became helpers. Even so, spirit rescue was slow work. A rescue circle might devote a whole evening to helping just one spirit.

Then, in the late 1970s, a talented young psychic named Terry O'Sullivan began to wonder whether there was not some quicker and more efficient method.

Terry's great grandmother had been a Romany gypsy, who had passed on her powers to her daughter, who in turn passed them on to Terry. When he went to London in his early 20s, he joined a rescue circle in Richmond, and spent the next few years developing his skills.

It was hard and sometimes frightening work - on one occasion, he reported being attacked by a poltergeist that clung to his back, glued to his powerful human aura like a nail to a magnet, only letting go when they were both exhausted.

It was towards 1980 that Terry stumbled on his new method of working. The root of the problem, he realised, is that earthbound spirits are living in a world that seems unreal to them.

Not knowing they are dead, they may go on hanging round the same place as when they were alive, and be baffled and irritated that other people are now living there - people they feel to be intruders.

Terry has often been asked to investigate a haunting, and found the puzzled and unhappy spirit of the last tenant, who believes that squatters have moved in. Terry then has to explain what has happened, and persuade the spirit to move on.

Crucially, living in their unreal world, 'earthbounds' see no clear distinction between thoughts and objects. And this, Terry realised, could provide him with the basis of a new rescue technique.

The idea came to him when he was gravely ill, and thought he was dying. He seemed to be at the entrance of a tunnel of light. But as he moved towards it, he saw his grandfather standing at the other end and making a gesture as if to say 'No'.

At the same time, Terry seemed to hear his grandfather tell him: 'Go back. It's not your time yet'. After that, he began to recover.

The experience made him realise that if he could only learn to show earthbound spirits this tunnel of light, it would be far easier than simply talking to them about it.

What he had to do was to try to conjure up his own vision of the 'lovely light', then turn himself into a kind of television transmitter to make the earthbound spirit see it too. When that happened, the spirit would plunge into it like a stranded fish diving into water.

Sometimes, when he had to deal with more than one spirit at a time - as when, on one occasion, he visited an American Civil War battlefield that was still full of the ghosts of fallen soldiers – Terry would conjure up the image of a staircase, extending between the two worlds. This method proved to be so successful that he now teaches it to all his students.

When I read reports of the tsunami ghosts, I understood the appalling implications of the disaster - thousands of bewildered people who were unaware that they were dead.

So it seemed only right that some-one should attempt to use Terry's techniques to help these poor souls.

On the day before the tsunami, a young British couple named Ross Pepperell and Katie Hancock had already decided to take a holiday in Thailand.

They eventually set out in mid-March, 2005, almost three months after the disaster had struck, and since both had been students of Terry O'Sullivan for three years, neither had any doubt about what to expect.

Their account of what followed is extraordinary, and many may find it hard to believe. But I personally have no doubts about their honesty and sincerity, and believe they may have achieved something quite remarkable on that tragic coast.

Ross and Katie are both natural 'psychics'. Ross made the discovery when he was 14, when he found that he could sometimes leave his body and walk around 'outside himself'.

Katie realised she was not like other people when she had premonitions of the future which often came true, but she was initially inclined to regard that as some odd kind of coincidence. Then she went to work in a shop selling crystals, and found that the crystals were causing her to develop healing powers.

When Ross and Katie set out from England, they had already heard the reports of the ghost sightings. And even as their plane circled Phuket airport, they sensed the activity was still going on.

Ross said later: 'I could feel the emotional shock of the disaster in my stomach. The airport itself had a heavy atmosphere that is often an indication of psychic disturbance and of haunting.'
I asked him: 'Could you see ghosts?'
'You don't see ghosts, you feel them'.
I was disappointed. 'You don't ever see them?'
'Oh yes. But that's after you've learned to feel them.

They're like a crowd of semi-visible people, and they're easiest to see in the half-light.'

Phi Phi was a beautiful island, and still is, in spite of the damage. Nothing can alter the beauty of the dawns and the sunsets, or of the vast seascape stretching towards Sumatra.

But for Ross and Katie, there was something not quite right - a feeling of tension in the air. And at dusk, they discovered, some of the invisible crowd of bewildered ghosts could become more visible to the living.

That is why Chaiyun Trisuwan, the manager of the Phi Phi Island Village resort, had to hire security guards to accompany his workers back home after dark.

Ross and Katie soon realised that the majority of spirits left on the island were foreigners - English, American, German. Just as the local people said, the Thai dead had been released by religious ceremonies, but the foreigners were unable to understand rituals in the Thai language.

The task of Ross and Katie was to perform the same service for these stranded foreigners. They could sense that, for these unhappy ghosts, merely to have someone who could see them and understand what had happened to them was a tremendous relief.

So the following day, Ross and Katie walked around the island. They were able to sense the presence of people who needed help, because in certain places there was a vibration of distress and emotional turmoil, trapped like tape recordings by powerful earth energies.

Dowsers can pick up these energies with a divining rod or pendulum, but after three years of practice Ross and Katie no longer needed these tools.

By now, both were permanently aware of the 'ghosts', most of them young people between 20 and 30, many of the girls in bikinis, the men in bathing shorts and flipflops. 'Spirits' see themselves - and are seen by others - in the clothes they died in.

Among the spirits were people who did know they were dead, but had no idea of what to do next or where to go. Ross and Katie were able to speak to them, exactly as you would speak to another person.

They told the spirits to be on the beach after dark, to watch out for a large bonfire, and to pass the word on to as many other spirits as they could.

That evening, Ross and Katie made an enormous bonfire of driftwood on the beach - there was no shortage of supplies - and then performed something called a 'land ritual', using dowsing techniques to purify and redirect the earth's energies.

This is a preliminary ceremony before opening a portal to the spirit world, that also establishes contact with helpers on 'the other side'. Ross estimates that there were over a thousand spirits on the beach.

Now came the difficult part. Ross calls it 'raising your vibrational rate' - clearing your mind of everyday thoughts and desires, and filling yourself with spiritual thoughts and emotions.

He and Katie worked at this in order to become fully aware of the connection between this world and the next. But it had to be done while maintaining contact with the vibrations of the spirits around them. They literally had to become a bridge.

Using the techniques taught them by Terry, they conjured up the vision of a portal in the form of a staircase, at the point where the land joined the sea. Its starting point appeared as a golden glow, just as Sir William Barrett's dying patient had described it.
The crowds began to move towards the light, like an audience leaving a cinema. Ross noted that a few late-comers even ran down the beach towards it. And in a surprisingly short time, it was all over, and only Ross, Katie, and some of their spirit helpers remained on an empty beach.

Ross asked them if there was anything further they could do, and the answer was 'no'. So they returned to their hotel room up the hill, with a pleasant sense of a job well done – and for their remaining few days' holiday on Phi Phi island, they were able to enjoy the sun and the waves in a new atmosphere of relaxation.

I have since read reports of several so-called 'exorcisms' performed by Chinese spiritualists on the tsunami beaches to achieve the same ends. In one, white robed monks from the Pu Ta

Gong sect chanted prayers, lit incense and offered sacrifices of food to the spirits.

Special offerings of pizza were included for foreign 'spirits', and paper clothes and money were burned to help in the passage to the afterworld.

Of course, Western sceptics will scoff, but the Thai people themselves would see nothing strange or unlikely about such ceremonies. To them, the existence of earthbound spirits is a fact of life - as is our duty to help them find peace.

Two years on from the tsunami, I sincerely hope that this has now happened. Author Colin Wilson.

DISMISSAL.
The peace of God, which passes all understanding, keep your heart and mind in the knowledge and love of God, and of his Son Jesus Christ our Lord; and the blessing of God almighty, the Father, the Son and the Holy Spirit, be among you and remain with you always. Amen. Go in peace and serve the Lord.
The Order for Holy Communion. Rite B, from The Alternative Service Book 1980.

CONCLUSION.
After more than 60 years of life, I have learnt that love is the ultimate development of the universe and that spiritual enlightenment, companionship, meditation, relaxation, belonging to a community and the **avoidance** of continuous stress and a hectic pace of life, are the closest things to a panacea for all ills. The most ubiquitous causes of ill-health and unhappiness seem to be a lifestyle of excess and social isolation.

My mnemonic for the day is always to;
Be invincibly good-natured,
deliberately unhurried,
time for everyone.
* * *

PART 2 REFERENCES.

Cohen, L. (1976). Educational Research in Classrooms and
   Schools: A manual of Materials and Methods. London:
   Harper & Row.

Eareckson, J. (1979). Joni. The unforgettable story of a
   young woman's struggle against quadriplegia and depression.
   London: Pickering & Inglis.

Laurentin, R. & Joyeux, H. (1987). Scientific & Medical Studies
   on the Apparitions At Medjugorje. Dublin: Veritas
   Publications.

Midgley, M. (2000). The Message of the Crucifixion: a
   spiritual guide to living with Myalgic Encephalomyelitis,
   Chronic Fatigue Syndrome and Fibromyalgia. Book and PAL
   video. Overton Studios Trust.

Plunkett, D. (1990). Queen of Prophets. The Spiritual Message
   of Medjugorje. London: Darton, Longman and Todd.

Rotholz, J. M. (2002). Chronic Fatigue Syndrome, Christianity,
   and Culture: Between God and an Illness. Haworth Press.

Tilby, A. (1992). Soul. An Introduction to the New
   Cosmology, - Time Consciousness and God. London: BBC
   Education.

Trower, P., Casey, A. & Dryden, W. (1988). Cognitive
   Behavioural Counselling in Action. London: Sage.

***

PART 3. A SCIENTIFIC PERSPECTIVE ON C.F.S./M.E.

INTRODUCTION

As said in the Introduction to this book, some years ago there were estimated to be between 100 and 200,000 people in the U.K. and about 1.4 million in the English speaking world suffering from C.F.S./M.E. assuming the same prevalence rate. Recently this estimate has increased by about 250 per cent to about half a million.

Many people with this disease are exhausted all the time, cannot work and suffer from anxiety and depression. The extent of interest in this illness can be measured in part by the apparent 35,600 C.F.S./M.E. websites in the U.K. and 115,000 related websites on the internet worldwide.

The Medical Research Council (M.R.C.) on their website www.mrc.ac.uk (go to this page and then insert 'cfs' into the search box and scan down for 'C.F.S./M.E. Research Strategy',) report the following:

"The independent scientific Research Advisory Group (R.A.G.) appointed by the Medical Research Council (M.R.C.) to make recommendations for developing a broad research strategy on Chronic Fatigue Syndrome/Myalgic Encephalomyelitis (C.F.S./M.E.), continues its consultation and is now seeking comments on its draft research strategy entitled:

'M.R.C. C.F.S./M.E. Research Advisory Group. C.F.S./M.E. Research Strategy'

This was published on 17 December 2002.

The work of the RAG has been underpinned by its recognition that C.F.S./M.E. is a real, serious and debilitating illness, endorsing the conclusions of the Report of the Chief Medical Officer's Independent Working Group. C.F.S./M.E. is clearly a complex illness about which we need to learn more through robust, high quality scientific research to improve knowledge, diagnosis, treatment, management of the condition and ultimately improve quality of life for those living with C.F.S./M.E.".

In the SUMMARY, the document says "...In view of the probable multiplicity of causal factors and the widely disparate findings so far reported, the M.R.C. C.F.S./M.E. Research Advisory Group considers that studies investigating potential causal pathways and mechanisms, whilst having merit, would not have the same immediate impact on increasing understanding of C.F.S./M.E., nor reducing the suffering of patients.

The M.R.C. C.F.S./M.E. Research Advisory Group considers it is appropriate to explore potential interventions for C.F.S./M.E. in the absence of knowledge of causation or pathogenesis."

In simpler words, potential treatments for the condition should be explored even though the causes of C.F.S./M.E. are not fully understood. This is a big step forward. Considerable scientific work has been completed on C.F.S./M.E. but rarely has it actually led to an improvement in the condition of sufferers.

The principal aims of this chapter and the book in general have been, to provide information directly relevant to improving the condition of sufferers and a concise source of information to avoid sufferers having to trawl through thousands of journals, books and websites.

It is suggested that the most important cutting edge research identifying one major cause of the illness, namely organophosphate pesticides and a potential treatment strategy, is described at:
http://osiris.sunderland.ac.uk/autism/ linking C.F.S./M.E., fibromyalgia, multiple chemical sensitivity and autism, to exposure to organophosphate pesticides.

In December 2002 I did a search and found, 175 books on C.F.S./M.E. on the Amazon.co.uk database of books, British Books in Print (BBIP) and the American Psychological Association. Below are a selection of the apparently most important.

Medical and health professionals, researchers, support agencies, patients, carers and libraries are the potential target purchasers and the titles cover C.F.S./M.E. **and Research methodology** (Sykes & Tyrrell, 2001); **the physical and medical aspects of C.F.S./M.E.** (Stoff & Pellegrino, 1992; Goldstein, 1996; Verillo & Gellman, 1998; Bell, 1995, 1999; Campling & Sharpe, 2000; De Meirleir, 2000; Duncan, 2000; Patarca-Montero, 2000a; Murray, 2001; Richardson, 2001; Taylor, et al., 2001; Duclos, 2002; Englebienne & De Meirleir, 2002; Voncannon, 2002; Abrams, 2003; Fennell,2003; Patarca-Montero, 2003a, b); **patient-centred approach** (Murdoch & Denz-Penhey, 2002); **the connection between C.F.S./M.E. and Fibromyalgia** (Brown, 1999; Teitelbaum, 1999; Berne, 2001); **C.F.S/M.E. self-help guides** (Lark, 1996; MacIntyre, 2001); information for mental health professionals to help their clients implement a **coping-oriented approach** to C.F.S./M.E. (Friedberg & Jason, 1998; Clinical Practice Guidelines, 2002); **environmental illnesses and C.F.S./M.E.** (Wittenberg, 1996); **effective treatments and management** (Jacobs, 1998; Mulrow, et al., 2001 Patarca-Montero, 2001; Taylor, 2002; Whiting et al., 2001); **alternative therapies and C.F.S./M.E.** (Murray, 1994; Cooper, 2000); **occupational Therapy for C.F.S./M.E.** (Cox, 2000); **biopsychosocial and wholistic approach** (Demitrack & Abbey, 1999; Jacobs, 2001; Nielson et al., 2001); **information for patients** (Patarca-Montero, 2000b; Parker, 2002); **sufferers' perspectives** (Munson, 2000; Petrie & Moss-Morris, 2000); **adolescents** (Brotherston, 2001); **parent's perspective and C.F.S./M.E.** (Davies, 2000); **Women and C.F.S./M.E.** (Martin, 1999); **Counselling for C.F.S./M.E.** (Chalder & Deale, 2000); and **Christian spirituality and C.F.S./M.E.** (Midgley, 2000; Rotholz, 2002).

In a concise but comprehensive paper Chaudhuri, Behan and Behan (1998) review the most important recent developments in C.F.S./M.E. research.

They say that the hallmark of this disorder is an overwhelming sense of tiredness, lack of energy and feeling of exhaustion, and is distinguishable from the peripheral fatigue which reduces maximum force output.

In this review, Chaudhuri et al. (1998) present the current state of knowledge on C.F.S./M.E. and suggest a possible pathogenesis (origin of the disease).

EPIDEMIOLOGY

The prevalence rate of C.F.S./M.E. in the United States is estimated as between 4-10 cases per 100,000 adults of 18 years and above. The prevalence of self-reported chronic fatigue may be several fold higher.

In the United Kingdom, a recent report estimated the population prevalence of C.F.S./M.E. in primary care to be 0.1-0.9% (100 – 900 cases per 100,000) based on the restrictive Center for Disease Control (CDC) criteria (excluding patients with psychiatric disorder).

In adolescents, the rate is slightly lower than that in adults; cases in children of less than seven years were very rare in 1988.

CLINICAL PRESENTATION

C.F.S./M.E. may develop after emotional or physical trauma, immunisation, ciguatera fish poisoning, or food poisoning with botulism.

Chaudhuri, Behan and Behan (1998) have recently described a neurobehavioural syndrome identical to C.F.S./M.E. associated with chronic exposure to low-dose organophosphate pesticides.

Malcolm Hooper Emeritus Professor of Medicinal Chemistry at Sunderland University has been researching a link between exposure to organo-phosphate pesticides (and organo-chlorine pesticides) and numerous medical conditions; Gulf War Syndrome, Fibromyalgia syndrome, Multiple Chemical Sensitivity, Autism and C.F.S./M.E., involving the brain, immune system, the gut and the HPA (hypothalamic-pituitary-adrenal) stress axis. The website below reports that organophosphate pesticides damage the digestion of dairy and wheat products. The suggested treatment is to omit these two food products from the diet and avoid exposure to organophosphate chemicals where possible. For more details of this research see website http://osiris.sunderland.ac.uk/autism/

Chaudhuri, Behan and Behan (1998) continue saying that it is possible that other environmental agents or toxins might serve as triggers of this disease. C.F.S./M.E. may also occur in association with sick building syndrome, after a prolonged period of stress, severe physical exercise, multiple chemical sensitivity and has been linked to silicone breast implants in women.

There may be more than **one** precipitating factor and co-existing disorders such as atopy (a form of allergy) or endometriosis (the presence of tissue similar to the lining of the uterus at other sites in the pelvis) may play a role in increasing host susceptibility to the development of C.F.S./M.E.

A significant proportion of C.F.S./M.E. patients attending Chaudhuri's clinic have asthma, eczema, atopy (a form of allergy) or serologic evidence of coeliac disease; the latter association may be important since cryptic gluten sensitivity may play a role in neurologic diseases.

A number of male patients have developed C.F.S./M.E. following an episode of epididymo-orchitis (infection and inflammation of the testicle). A recent study of Persian Gulf War veterans has now concluded that the symptoms are identical to C.F.S./M.E. and to Fibromyalgia.

Physical symptoms.
Chaudhuri, Behan and Behan (1998) report that paroxysmal (sudden violent) attacks of chest pain and sweating are two symptoms commonly found in this condition. Indeed, many patients with C.F.S./M.E. were originally referred to them by cardiologists as having syndrome X (anginal chest pain with normal coronary arteries). Unexplained attacks of severe sweating, typically during the night, are common.

Of the neuropsychiatric findings, some patients develop hypergraphia, i.e. keeping detailed records and long descriptions of all their symptoms, and come to the clinic with interminable notes. (I the author, have kept a record of my activity every 15 minutes throughout the day since 1988 and still do this as a way of seeing patterns of events which help in the self-management of the illness and the avoidance of relapses. It seems that other C.F.S, sufferers do similarly. For me it was a desperate attempt to get some control and predictability in my life, for without these, nothing can be planned for the individual or their family). However, patients never have *anhedonia* (loss of pleasure in life) or the suicidal symptoms of typical depressive illness although a pre-morbid psychiatric abnormality (depression-prone) may be evident. (I the author **did** experience anhedonia and obsessional thoughts of suicide).

Factors that improve or worsen fatigue.
Pregnancy is the only time when women experience significant improvement of their symptoms but there is often severe 'rebound fatigue' in the early puerperium (the period of about six weeks after childbirth).

A variety of specific and non-specific factors appear to make the fatigue and other associated symptoms worse, including a heavy meal, a prolonged hot bath or alcohol. Some patients get such a distressing reaction to the smallest amount of alcohol ingested that they abstain entirely.

Both physical and mental effort can worsen fatigue in C.F.S./M.E. There is an exacerbation of both physical and mental symptoms during menstruation: with worsening of fatigue and myalgia (pain in the muscles), and women whose menstrual phase had not been previously marked by hyperirritability and emotional tension complained that they could not control themselves and flew into rages at what they realised were really insignificant frustrations or annoyances.

Clinical signs
Patients with C.F.S./M.E. are not permanently wheelchair-bound. Patients in wheelchairs without other disease, who have been diagnosed as having C.F.S./M.E., on detailed scrutiny turn out to have a primary personality disorder; these are typically young women characterised by avoidance of social interaction and craving for assistance, even for toilet care and feeding. They prefer to be alone in their own rooms with the curtains drawn, avoiding any contact with bright light because of photophobia. This is called, 'Miss Haversham syndrome' (referring to the well known Charles Dickens character)(Chaudhuri, Behan and Behan 1998).

DIFFERENTIAL DIAGNOSIS
When fatigue is combined with myalgia (pain in the muscles) a long list of differential diagnoses can be generated (Table 3.1.) which must be excluded by appropriate tests before a diagnosis of C.F.S./M.E. is made. In practice, perhaps the most important differential diagnosis of C.F.S./M.E. is depression. Depressed patients commonly complain of fatigue. However, depressive features **not** usually present in C.F.S./M.E. are:
   (1) recurrent thoughts of death or suicidal ideation;
   (2) markedly diminished interest or pleasure in all, or almost all daily activities (anhedonia);
   (3) excessive or inappropriate guilt.

223

Hallucinations and delusions are not a feature of C.F.S./M.E.

There is an overlap of C.F.S./M.E. symptoms and somatisation disorder (physical symptoms occurring without an apparent physical disorder), in which the physical complaints begin before the age of 30 years and generally have been present for five years or more. The majority of C.F.S./M.E. patients have no evidence of hyperventilation. Because of the abundance of information currently available about C.F.S./M.E. in the lay media, the Munchausen phenomenon, i.e. a fictitious shamming of the syndrome, may occur with patients purporting to suffer from C.F.S.

Post-polio fatigue
Fatigue is the most commonly reported, most debilitating post-polio sequel affecting 1.63 million polio survivors in America alone. Its features are similar to those of C.F.S./M.E. Autopsy studies performed more than 50 years ago revealed frequent, severe lesions in the reticular activating system (RAS) of the brain in post-polio patients. (The RAS is concerned with the level of consciousness, from sleep, relaxation to full alertness. The system integrates information from the senses, the brain and autonomic nervous system and determines the level of overall activity). Like fatigue, hypotension (very low blood pressure) is common to both C.F.S./M.E. and post-polio cases, possibly due to dysfunction of the brain stem and hypothalamus (Chaudhuri, Behan and Behan, 1998).

LABORATORY FINDINGS
Routine laboratory tests seldom reveal any specific abnormality in the chronic phase of the illness though some do occur more often than would occur by chance (Table 3.2).

Immunology
Non-specific immunological abnormalities have been widely reported in this condition.

Tests for heterophile antibody (the body's response to infection) were found to be positive in an average of 15% patients in pooled data. No difference has been recorded in the serology testing (blood serum) for Lyme disease (B. burgdorferi antibodies) between patients and controls. There is also incontrovertible evidence that C.F.S./M.E. patients suffer from atopy (a form of allergy in which the hypersensitivity reaction may be distant from the region of contact with the substance – *atopen* – responsible) more frequently than the normal population, for which an aberrant cytokine response (of the immune system) is a possible explanation.

(I would interject here to indicate that a course of antibiotics kills not only the infection (not viral infection) being targeted but also all of the benign bacteria in the intestines. These benign bacteria make up 60 per cent of the individual's immune system; leaving them vulnerable to new infection and possibly C.F.S./M.E. without them).

Virology (the study of viruses)
It was suggested that C.F.S./M.E. could be an acquired metabolic myopathy (disease of the muscles) induced by persistent virus infection. Early investigation linked EBV (i.e. Epstein-Barr Virus, the causative agent for infectious mononucleosis – glandular fever) and C.F.S./M.E. -the so-called chronic mononucleosis syndrome - but subsequent studies have failed to substantiate this. Persistence of enteroviruses was considered to be an attractive hypothesis for fatigue, myalgia and non-specific muscle abnormalities.

There are similarities between C.F.S./M.E. and post-polio syndrome. However, enteroviruses and other putative candidates for persistent virus infection, such as human herpes viruses, cytomegalovirus or measles virus have not been identified in current research. **Similarly, no evidence exists that C.F.S./M.E. is due to persistent retroviral infection, whether caused by HIV or other human T cell lymphotrophic viruses.**

Table 3.1.
Other disorders associated with Chronic Fatigue Syndrome.

Anaemia (reduction in quantity of oxygen-carrying pigment haemoglobin in the blood)   (all causes).

Autoimmune diseases (Inflammation and destruction of tissues by the body's own antibodies)   (Sjogren's syndrome – dry mouth caused by wasting of salivary glands, polymyositis – disease of muscles).

Drug-induced conditions   (alcohol, sedatives, interferon – a substance produced by cells infected with a virus that can inhibit viral growth, HMG-Coenzyme A-inhibitors– a class of drugs).

Endocrine disorders   (hypothyroidism – under-functioning thyroid gland; hyperparathyroidism – overactivity of the parathyroid glands, Addison's disease – inadequate secretion of corticosteroid hormones by the adrenal glands; polyglandular insufficiency).

Metabolic disorders   (haemochromatosis – a hereditary disorder involving excessive absorption of iron, metabolic myopathies – disease of the muscles).

Malignancy & Paraneoplastic syndromes (symptoms and signs occurring in Patients with cancer but not due directly to the cancer)   (limbic encephalitis – inflammation of the brain caused by an infection).

Neurological diseases
(diseases of the nervous system)

(multiple sclerosis – the myelin sheath of nerves of the brain and spinal cord are damaged, demyelinating neuropathies – diseases of peripheral nerves, Parkinson's disease – a disorder characterised by tremor, rigidity and poverty of spontaneous movements, multiple system atrophy – wasting away of organs or tissues).

Obesity

Sarcoidosis
(lymph nodes are enlarged and small fleshy nodules develop in the lungs, liver and spleen)

Sleep disorders

(narcolepsy – extreme tendency to fall asleep, obesity - hypoventilation syndrome – breathing at an abnormally slow rate).

Systemic infection

(viral, bacterial, fungal, parasitic or protozoal).

Vasculitides
(plural of vasculitis, also called angiitis - patchy inflammation of the walls of small blood vessels)

(SLE – systemic lupus erythematosis, giant cell arteritis – inflammatory disease affecting the muscle walls of arteries, especially the scalp, Wegener's granulomatosis – small rounded outgrowths in the nasal passages, lungs and kidneys and arteritis).

Withdrawal syndromes

***

Chaudhuri, Behan and Behan (1998) carried out experiments to analyse tissue from patients with C.F.S./M.E., affective (relating to the emotions) disorders and normal controls, for Borna disease virus (B.D.V) since there is some circumstantial evidence that B.D.V can affect the central nervous system of man causing a variety of different psychiatric illness. All samples from healthy and depressed controls were negative, and only two C.F.S./M.E. patients proved positive for BDV. While it is clear that infection with any of these agents may result in C.F.S./M.E., and even though viral persistence can be documented in some using molecular cloning techniques, it is not now thought that such **persistence** is contributory to the genesis (origin or development) of the illness (Chaudhuri, Behan and Behan, 1998).

Viral persistence can occur because N.K. (natural killer) cells of the immune system, that normally kill such cells have been damaged by OPs in some C.F.S./M.E. sufferers. (I would suggest that the virus reappears only when a relapse occurs. It may be that within a few days of a relapse the virus disappears apart from within brain and muscle cells where it remains dormant. Therefore it is important for C.F.S./M.E. patients to remember the date of their last relapse as their biology may change over time).

Table 3.2. Abnormal laboratory findings in C.F.S.

Haematology:

(the study of blood)

Leucopenia – a reduction of white blood cells leucocytes in the blood.

relative lymphocytosis – an increase in the number of lymphocytes (a variety of white blood cell) in the blood often due to viruses.

monocytosis (~30%) – an increase in the number of monocytes (a variety of white blood cell in the blood often due to infection.

Raised ESR (~15%) – **erythrocyte sedimentation**

rate (the rate at which red blood cells, erythrocytes, settle out of suspension in blood plasma. The ESR increases if the level of certain proteins in the plasma rises, as in rheumatic diseases, chronic infections, and malignant diseases and thus provides a valuable screening test for these conditions.

Reduced serum folate (~10%) – serum is the fluid that separates from blood plasma that is allowed to stand.

Abnormal RBC (Red Blood Cell) morphology ('nondiscocytic erythrocytes') – mis-shapen erythrocytes.

Biochemistry: Elevated LFT (Liver Function Test) and CK (~5-20%),
Reduced intracellular carnitine,
Elevated levels of serum angiotensin-converting enzyme (ACE) – angiotensin is a protein in the blood, derived from a plasma protein and released by the action of an enzyme renin from the kidneys, that causes an increase in output of aldosterone from the adrenal cortex. Angiotensin is also capable of causing constriction of blood vessels, thus raising blood pressure,
Reduced 24-hour urinary cortisol.

Autoantibodies: Anti-thyroid (microsomal - a type of antibodies)
(antibodies & anti-gliadin positivity (~10-30%),
formed against Low concentrations of antinuclear antibody
one of the and Rheumatoid Factor (the presence of which
body's own helps diagnose rheumatoid arthritis
components in False positive VDRL (~1-8%).
autoimmune
disease)

CSF: Faint oligoclonal bands (~1-2%) – antibodies.
(Cerebrospinal
fluid)

ECG: Non-specific ST and T wave changes.
(Electrocardio-
gram,electrical

229

activity of the
heart).

EEG: Slowing of background rhythm
(Electroenceph-   usually over temporal regions.
alogram,
electrical
activity of
brain).

***

Genetic studies.
Chaudhuri, Behan and Behan (1998) report finding the common
mitochondrial DNA (mtDNA) deletion in two of eight cases.

Despite the lack of evidence of a genetic basis for C.F.S./M.E.,
Chaudhuri, Behan and Behan (1998) have seen from time to time,
more than one member of the same family being affected by this
illness and the process of a subtle genetic predisposition possibly
related to maternal (mitochondrial) inheritance, cannot totally be
dismissed. (I, the author think that some familial cases of
C.F.S./M.E. may be due to exposure of the family members to
organophosphate pesticide (OPs) in head lice shampoo. Whole
families use the shampoo).

MUSCLE STUDIES
Bioenergetic.
Chaudhuri, Behan and Behan (1998) say that ^{31}P nuclear magnetic
resonance spectroscopy (NMRS) provides an excellent method for
continuous in vivo monitoring of intracellular energy metabolism
in skeletal muscles. NMRS studies have shown a significant
reduction in the exercise capacity in C.F.S./M.E. accompanied by
excessively early intracellular acidification. Both increased
acidification relative to phosphocreatine (PCr) depletion and
reduced acidification have been found in C.F.S./M.E.

A significant reduction in **aerobic** metabolism was noted in PCr recovery. Skeletal muscle NMRS studies in syndrome X (having anginal chest pain with normal coronary arteries) have reported similar underlying abnormalities, supporting the clinical observation of Chaudhuri, Behan and Behan (1998), that C.F.S./M.E. and syndrome X could have a similar metabolic disorder. Reduced oxidative muscle metabolism in C.F.S./M.E. patients has recently been confirmed in another study which compared 22 C.F.S./M.E. patients to normal sedentary subjects before and two days after a maximal treadmill test. Muscle oxidative capacity was measured as the maximal rate of post-exercise PCr re-synthesis in the calf muscles using ^{31}P NMRS. The oxidative capacity (maximal rate of Adenosine Triphosphate [ATP] synthesis) was significantly reduced in C.F.S./M.E. patients as opposed to controls. No further changes however were seen in the post-exercise period.

Cell culture
Aerobic metabolism was evaluated in myoblast (a cell that develops into a muscle fibre) cultures established from muscle biopsies of 16 typical cases of C.F.S./M.E. compared to ten normal controls. There was a statistically significant broader range of lactate/pyruvate (L/P) ratios, a measure of the redox function in the patients' myoblast cultures, compared to controls. Culture from 10 of the 16 cases showed mild defects of **aerobic metabolism** with myoblasts from two patients showing increased L/P ratios suggestive of a defect in **oxidative phosphorylation** while eight had decreased ratios consistent with a mild **deficiency in pyruvate dehydrogenase**. Mitochondrial volume was not significantly increased and no mtDNA (mitochondrial DNA) rearrangements were present. One of the patients with decreased L/P ratio had biopsy findings suggestive of a **mild mitochondrial myopathy**.

EXERCISE
Since by definition C.F.S./M.E. patients experience profound deterioration of their fatigue and muscle symptoms after exercise a number of studies have looked at post-exercise motor performance.

In an incremental treadmill protocol (walking to exhaustion) C.F.S./M.E. patients showed a lower VO_2 max (maximum volume of oxygen consumed) as compared with controls in the absence of any cardiopulmonary abnormality. Other studies on exercise performance and fatiguability could not demonstrate any difference between patients or controls though about a third of C.F.S./M.E. cases had an abnormal lactate response and tachycardia (increase in heart rate above normal). Chaudhuri, Behan and Behan (1998) carried out repetitive isometric quadriceps exercise (knee extension against fixed resistance) in a well-characterised group of C.F.S./M.E. patients and compared their performance with matched controls. Whilst there was no significant difference between the groups during the first part of the exercise, a markedly rapid decline in quadriceps tension was evident in the patient group at 200 minutes (3 hours 20 minutes) and on the following day (after 24 hours) during recovery. This is the first objective evidence of post-exercise fatigue in C.F.S.

OTHER LABORATORY FINDINGS
Nerve conduction studies(NCS) and needle electromyography(EMG). Several studies have shown that motor and sensory NCS are normal in all cases of C.F.S./M.E.

Table tilt testing
Chaudhuri, Behan and Behan (1998) also report that an abnormal response to upright table tilt was found in 22 of the 23 patients with C.F.S./M.E. as against 4 out of 14 controls. During the first 40 minutes of the upright tilt, symptomatic patients maintained stable heart rate and blood pressure but subsequently, there was an abrupt decrease of both the heart rates and blood pressure, and development of severe presyncopal symptoms (warmth, light-headedness, nausea and sweating). This phenomenon, called neurally-mediated hypotension (NMH - arterial blood pressure is abnormally low), is considered to be due to an abnormal cardiovascular reflex mechanism in C.F.S./M.E. patients.

Neuroimaging

Regional cerebral hypoperfusion (low level of blood flow in the brain), however, was noted by Chaudhuri, Behan and Behan (1998) and others in the Single Photon Emission Computed Tomographic (SPECT) cerebral-flow scans. The hypoperfused areas were cortical and subcortical, typically involving the temporal lobes in Chaudhuri, Behan and Behan (1998) study, while hypoperfusion of the brain stem was reported in another study. No consistent pattern has emerged but it is clear that patients with C.F.S./M.E., both children and adults, may have multiple areas of regional cerebral hypoperfusion.

ROLE OF TOXINS IN C.F.S./M.E.

Chaudhuri, Behan and Behan (1998) observe that few studies have addressed the issue of toxins in producing C.F.S./M.E. Chronic, low-dose organophosphate pesticide exposure is one of the suggested toxic models of C.F.S./M.E. Organophosphates (and carbamates) are potent inhibitors of neuronal acetylcholinesterase (involved in nerve transmission) and long-term neurological abnormalities after exposure to these agents are well recognised.

Patients who develop C.F.S./M.E. after chronic low-dose organophosphate exposure are extremely sensitive to such compounds, and develop catastrophic fatigue and cardiac arrhythmias when exposed even to a minute amount. (Since OP pesticide residues are frequently found in many foods such as bread and cereals, exposure to such minute amounts might happen regularly for some patients).

According to Chaudhuri, Behan and Behan (1998) further evidence for a cholinergic role (namely involving the neurotransmitter chemical acetylcholine) in C.F.S./M.E. patients comes from the observation that the survivors of food-borne botulism during the epidemic of late 1980s in North England and Wales developed symptoms of C.F.S./M.E. over the following years. Botulinum toxin is known to selectively act on the pre-synaptic cholinergic nerve terminals inhibiting the release of synaptic acetylcholine. C.F.S./M.E. also occurs after ciguatera fish poisoning; the toxin is a potent inactivator of the neuronal sodium channels. **Organochlorines** have been postulated to have an aetiologic role in C.F.S./M.E. and one study documented a higher level of total organochlorine and hexachlorobenzene (HCB) in patients who developed symptoms of C.F.S./M.E. after organochlorine exposure, as opposed to controls. Chronic lead poisoning can have an identical presentation to C.F.S./M.E. Patients with multiple chemical sensitivity (MCS) share symptoms with C.F.S./M.E. and are sensitive to a large number of chemicals even in very small doses. The 'supersensitivity' phenomenon that characterises the symptomatic C.F.S./M.E. patients who develop the illness after exposure to one or more chemicals is possibly mediated by an olfactory-limbic mechanism.

HYPOTHALAMIC DYSFUNCTION IN C.F.S./M.E.

"Hypothalamic dysfunction" refers to abnormalities found in the functioning of the hypothalamus region in the brain.

Chaudhuri, Behan and Behan (1998) list the symptoms that suggest hypothalamic involvement in C.F.S./M.E. as:
(1)   fatigue;
(2)   sleep disorders (somnolence and sleep rhythm reversal);
(3)   abnormal sweating;
(4)   altered temperature;
(5)   poikilothermia, which is the inability to exert fine control over the internal temperature by physiological means;
(6)   mood disorder;
(7)   changes in appetite and craving for certain foods;
(8)   weight changes and idiopathic cyclic oedema (excessive
(9)   accumulation of fluid in the body tissues);
(10) menstrual dysfunction;
(11) abnormal hypothalamic arginine-vasopressin secretion and water metabolism in C.F.S./M.E. patients;
(12) idiopathic cyclic oedema, a condition frequently accompanying C.F.S./M.E. in women, is associated with

abnormalities in the regulation of gonadal hormones and prolactin, presumably due to hypothalamic dysfunction.

Chaudhuri, Behan and Behan (1998) found that in the post-polio fatigue syndrome, abnormal prolactin release was documented with a correlation between the prolactin level and the severity of fatigue symptoms.

An abnormality of the hypothalamic-pituitary-adrenal (HPA) axis in C.F.S./M.E. has been demonstrated according to Chaudhuri, Behan and
Behan (1998). They suggest that in C.F.S./M.E. there is a pituitary-deficient hypo-cortisolic state.

(ACTH - Adreno-cortico-tropic hormone). All patients had normal levels of circulating ACTH but showed an evening rise as compared to normal subjects. The pituitary ACTH release was blunted in response to exogenous C.R.H. (Corticotropin Releasing Hormone or Factor), but this is not unique to C.F.S./M.E. and is found in various other conditions associated with stress and in the overtrained athlete. Presumably, this reflects a lack of adaptation of the HPA axis to chronic stress which may be a key trigger for the development and perpetuation of C.F.S./M.E. There is also evidence to suggest that C.F.S./M.E. patients have a reduced volume of their adrenal glands, which could indicate a hypofunctioning HPA.

NEUROENDOCRINE ABNORMALITIES IN C.F.S./M.E.
Chaudhuri, Behan and Behan (1998) continue by reporting that the neuroendocrine axis assessment has traditionally been considered one of the best and safest approaches for assessing specific neurotransmitter functions in the central nervous system. A variety of abnormalities have been described in the neuroendocrine functions in C.F.S./M.E. patients (Table 3.3.) of which the most consistent is the evidence of upregulated serotonin and acetylcholine activity, and reduced sensitivity (down-regulated) to

norepinephrine, glucocosteroids and vasopressin have been claimed.

RECENT RESEARCH
Resting energy expenditure in C.F.S./M.E.
Resting energy expenditure (REE) is the energy expended by an awake, alert subject in the post-absorptive state (i.e. after absorption of food and fluid). REE accounts for between 60% and 90% of the total energy expenditure and any increase in REE, in the absence of compensatory increase in diet, should result in there being less energy available for other physical activities.

Table 3.3.
Neuroendocrine abnormalities in C.F.S.

Supersensitivity to: serotonin (5 HT)
(i.e. up-regulated   acetylcholine
 receptors)

Subsensitivity to: norepinephrine
(i.e. down-regulated   glucocorticoids
 receptors)   (possibly) vasopressin

Chaudhuri, Behan and Behan (1998) carried out a study to investigate REE in patients with C.F.S./M.E. and healthy controls. They found a significant rise in REE in 5/11 C.F.S./M.E. patients as compared to controls. This finding offers one possible contributor to fatigue in some C.F.S./M.E. patients in that the energy available for physical activity is being diverted to fulfil the increased energy requirements of the presumably metabolically overactive tissue.

Thallium scans and C.F.S./M.E.
Myocarditis, was common in an analysis of 1,000 patients with C.F.S./M.E. seen in Glasgow over the past 20 years. There was a frequent association with acute chest pain resembling an acute

coronary event in the development of C.F.S./M.E. For these patients heart investigations were normal but, on subsequent clinical follow-up, they were indistinguishable from patients who had had a viral infection and went on to develop C.F.S./M.E. A significant number of cases of this so-called syndrome X therefore strongly resemble C.F.S./M.E. Furthermore, nuclear magnetic resonance spectroscopy studies of **skeletal muscle** in patients with syndrome X show abnormalities identical to those found in patients with C.F.S./M.E. according to Chaudhuri, Behan and Behan (1998).

They report that cardiac thallium-201 SPECT scans on a series of syndrome X patients revealed abnormalities in a significant proportion; the intravenous injection of radioactive thallium-201 rapidly accumulates intracellularly in a similar fashion to potassium. The abnormalities seen in the scans are not due to coronary stenosis (narrowing of the arteries supplying blood to the heart) since all these patients have angiographically-normal coronary systems. One group of researchers proposed that the defect in the uptake of thallium-201 could be due to a change in cell metabolism resulting from abnormal ion loss and not to microvascular ischaemia (an inadequate flow of blood to the heart, caused by constriction or blockage of the blood vessels supplying it).

Chaudhuri, Behan and Behan (1998) carried out scans on a small group of well characterised C.F.S./M.E. patients without any symptoms of chest pain. None of the patients had any cardiac symptoms at the time of their scan but image analysis revealed moderate perfusion (flow) defects in the left ventricles of 70% of the patients studied.

Their basic hypothesis is that a precipitating event, such as a viral infection (or other ionophore), can cause the muscle cell, heart cell, or neurone cell membrane to lose potassium ions and cause increased ATPase (Adenosine triphosphatease – an enzyme involved in energy production in cells) activity in an attempt to maintain cellular integrity.

Ionophores are one of a range of small organic molecules facilitating ion movement across a cell membrane. They either enclose the ion and diffuse through the membrane (e.g. valinomycin-K^+) or form pore-channels in the lipid bilayer (e.g. gramicidin), in which case water molecules are allowed through too. Some are products of micro-organisms and may have adverse effects upon cells of competing species.

Given the symptom overlap between C.F.S./M.E. and syndrome X, and similar thallium-201 scan findings in both syndromes, the cellular transport defect proposed to explain the abnormal myocardial thallium-201 uptake in syndrome X may also be relevant to the presently reported findings in C.F.S.

In trying to relate these findings to myself, I, the author recall having had many heart symptoms like extrasystolies (an extra noticeable heart beat) and rapid heart beating especially just before falling asleep. I was referred to a physician at a hospital who diagnosed cardiac side-effects from the amitriptyline I was prescribed. My ECG (electrocardiogram) was normal otherwise. I was prescribed timolol and the symptoms resolved. This is some evidence for the hypothesis.

A PAPER BY DR. MYHILL
"C.F.S./M.E. is Heart Failure Secondary to Mitochondrial Malfunction". www.drmyhill.co.uk

It describes problems C.F.S./M.E. sufferers may have with mitochondria and suggests food supplements aimed at ameliorating them.

Some dietitians and nutritionist have commented on the extremely high doses of the food supplements (notwithstanding the expense) recommended by Dr. Myhill. I tried out the mitochondrial supplements by taking the dosage **recommended by the manufacturer** adding one each week until taking them all at the same time. After about a month I found no positive effect until the last supplement was started namely the D-Ribose often called Corvalen. This did given me more energy. I then left off each supplement and noticed no lose of energy until the D-Ribose was withdrawn showing that that was the active supplement for me. However after taking D-Ribose for a further month I found the increased energy resulted in more symptoms of depression occurring, which normally only happen when I have over exerted myself physically or mentally. D-Ribose was allowing me to over exert myself, so I withdrew it to try again later in a more carefully controlled trial. Dr. Myhill's recommended dosages may be necessary for optimal effect.

AN HYPOTHESIS
I have a hypothesis concerning two of the possible causes of fatigue in C.F.S./M.E patients. I would suggest that **anaerobic** (low utilization of oxygen) activity causes little or no production of serotonin, but instead depletes it in the brain. For normal people any activity probably generates some serotonin. However, in both groups **aerobic** (oxygen is utilized) activity generates serotonin.

Serotonin
Figure 3.1. is a schematic representation of how serotonin seems to be utilized in the brain. Thinking, emotions, hunger, thirst, sex drive, temperature control, aerobic and anaerobic activity are all mediated by serotonin in the hypothalamus.

Resting and sleep appear to be associated with increased levels of serotonin. Serotonin is likely to be high early in the morning and fall to a low in the evening. Therefore aerobic exercise early in the day is likely to increase it but exercise in the evening may consume the last of the serotonin and tip a C.F.S./M.E. sufferer into draining the reserve and drawing on the production site of serotonin.

Figure 3.1. A schematic diagram of serotonin utilization.

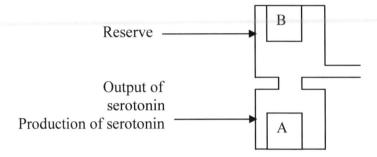

It is suggested that aerobic exercise requires enough serotonin in the reserve to carry out the exercise itself before it leads to an increase in serotonin production. If the reserve B is empty then any exercise or activity will draw serotonin from the production site damaging and reducing serotonin production excessively. For the C.F.S/M.E. sufferer, this can cause a relapse and sometimes reactivation of the virus and may take months or years from which to recover, if at all.

Antidepressants drugs like amitriptyline slow consumption of serotonin in activity and allow the reserve to replenish. Dropping the dosage of amtriptyline will allow increased consumption of serotonin again drawing on the reserve and then the production site if not enough time has elapsed to refill the reserve. This again could cause a relapse.   For C.F.S./M.E. sufferers anaerobic activity seems to consume serotonin and to have little positive effect on serotonin production.

Aerobic exercise can, it is suggested so stimulate serotonin production in a C.F.S./M.E. sufferer that if too much exercise is engaged in, production triggers viral replication and the onset of a relapse. This can only be avoided by a very gradual increase in aerobic exercise.

In C.F.S./M.E. as said earlier, the serotonin receptors in the hypothalamus have been damaged causing them to be up-regulated; supersensitive to serotonin and therefore causing low output of serotonin production. Also potassium loss from neurones is suggested as the second major problem causing fatigue in C.F.S./M.E.

Potassium loss

As said earlier, potassium ions K^+ are being lost from heart muscle cells and possibly muscle and brain cells, (including serotonin, acetylcholine and steroid receptor cells in the hypothalamus and norepinephrine, glucocorticoid and vasopressin receptor cells damaging their function i.e. causing under functioning, fatiguing prematurely or giving a changed output of peptides).

Normally in cells, potassium ions are pumped in and sodium ions pumped out of the cell by an ATPase pump. Gated potassium channels are closed when the neurone is at rest, but open when the neurone is active. Most potassium channels have no gates and are open.

So when a C.F.S./M.E. sufferer is at rest potassium loss is lowest and energy used by the ATPase pump at a low, but when active the loss of K+ is greater. This takes energy via the ATPase pump. The Nernst Equation gives the voltage difference between the outside and inside of the cell membrane and shows the higher the temperature the greater the voltage and the greater the electrical force expelling K^+ ions from the cell. It is suggested that when a C.F.S./M.E. sufferer is hot i.e. in a hot bath, sunbathing or has a temperature with viral infection, K^+ ion loss from cells will be greater and require a considerable amount of energy to pump them back into the cell – resulting in greater fatigue. This might explain why I have sometimes experienced panic attacks after a long period sunbathing, possibly due to the body's secretion of adrenaline to generate increased blood glucose as a result, and this adrenaline being experienced as anxiety.

Figure 3.2 Sodium/potassium ion pump.

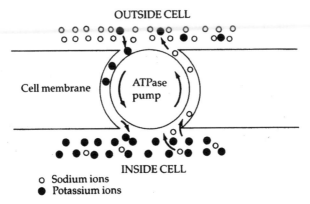

Diagram from Thompson 1993 p.59.

As can be seen in the diagram in Figure 3.2 sodium ions are involved and this may have a connection with sodium levels and low blood pressure found in some C.F.S./M.E. patients.

Low blood pressure in C.F.S./M.E. sufferers might be associated with low levels of intake of salt, a source of sodium ions, which have a positive charge and are outside the cell. When sodium levels are low, potassium ions which also have a positive charge will leak out more easily and will require more energy to pump them back into the cells than if there were higher, more normal levels of sodium ions outside the cell. The higher levels of sodium ions outside the cell associated with normal blood pressure will **repel** the potassium ions trying to leak out of the cell, because both have a positive charge, and positively charged ions repel each other. It is suggested that this repellent force would result in a slower leakage of potassium ions from cells and assist in the pumping required to return the potassium ions to the cells. Increasing their salt intake to restore blood pressure to normal may greatly assist the problem of leaking potassium ions and thereby reduce fatigue for C.F.S./M.E. sufferers.

Chaudhuri, Behan and Behan (1998) found that C.F.S./M.E. patients had higher resting energy expenditure (REE) than controls. This was based on their total body potassium (TBK) level. It may be that the constant energy required to correct the level of potassium in C.F.S/M.E patients' neurones causes this high REE. The question is, did the C.F.S./M.E. patients have a high REE before they became ill with C.F.S./M.E.? I, have always been warm as if burning much energy, **before** I became ill with C.F.S./M.E. I speculate about the fact that I have suffered very badly from bouts of flu in the past and may have suffered incremental damage to neurone cell membranes as a result of viral infections. It may be that a final bout precipitates C.F.S./M.E. Taking essential fatty acids in Efamol seems to have resulted in some improvement in my illness. Again one speculates whether EFAs have any role in such cell processes.

It may be the constant ATPase pump recovering lost K^+, that is an indirect cause of the hypoglycaemia (low blood glucose) many C.F.S./M.E. sufferers experience.

I would suggest that C.F.S./M.E. patients should avoid getting chilled or cold, because energy will be wasted trying to maintain body temperature and less energy will be available for the ATPase pump needed to restore potassium levels. Poikilothermia, which is the inability to exert fine control over the internal temperature by physiological means was noted earlier as a symptom of C.F.S./M.E. Problems in controlling serotonin levels in the hypothalamus disrupts body temperature control in C.F.S./M.E. anyway.

Potassium loss and restoration, I would suggest is experienced as muscle tingling and not initially fatigue by a sufferer. This I think comes a little later. Indulging in physical exercise to a greater extent than normal, like for example, pushing a pushchair through long grass, results in muscle cells not normally used becoming activated. Activated muscle cells require activation of more neurones which will consequently lose more potassium resulting in greater feelings of fatigue. Tingling of the muscles might ensue, but so too might hunger as the body burns energy in order to pump back lost potassium.

The loss of potassium ions during activity might explain why fatigue in C.F.S./M.E. is often delayed until sometime after the activity. It may be because:

1. potassium gradually gets lost from many cells during activity, but
2. once the activity has stopped the body will use much energy pumping the potassium ions back into cells – and hence increasing fatigue will be felt across this time until a low point when all of ions have been recovered. From then on the fatigue will gradually improve during rest, but if not enough rest occurs then the individual will be left feeling continually fatigued.

Anaerobic and aerobic activity.
Researchers say that anaerobic metabolism is important for the provision of energy for mechanical activity, and for all muscles during the initial period of exercise before the exercise-stimulated increase in blood supply occurs which increases the oxygen supply to the muscles.

Therefore in any aerobic activity the first 10 to 20 minute period involves only anaerobic metabolism. It is only after this period that aerobic metabolism involving oxygen begins to take place. It is thus suggested that the C.F.S./M.E. sufferer should undertake graded activity (best measured in gentle walking) until 20 minutes is achieved before attempting aerobic activity like brisker walking, table tennis, jogging for a few seconds to a minute etc. which should themselves be increased gradually a few minutes at a time.

There is a loss of K^+ ions from muscle cells during hypoxia (a deficiency of oxygen possibly caused by sustained inactivity and consequent poor breathing movements, resulting in anaerobic metabolism) or ischaemia (an inadequate flow of blood caused by a constriction or blockage of the blood vessels supplying that region of the body). This loss reduces the rate of glycolysis (and therefore the production of energy) because of the dependence of the kinase enzymes, on K^+ ions, for maximal activity. This loss of K^+ ions plus the additional loss due to damage to the cell membrane in C.F.S./M.E. is another possible factor in their fatigue when anaerobic metabolism or activity is occurring.

Since loss of K^+ ions occurs during hypoxia, a method of reducing this loss for C.F.S./M.E. sufferers might be oxygenation of the muscle cells through aerobic metabolism and activity. In both aerobic and anaerobic metabolism glucose is first converted into pyruvate. However, in anaerobic metabolism the pyruvate is converted into lactate, whereas in aerobic metabolism it is converted to acetyl-CoA (acetyl-coenzyme A).

Lactate that diffuses into the bloodstream is carried to the liver where it is taken up and reconverted to glucose in the process known as gluconeogenesis.

It has already been mentioned earlier in this chapter that C.F.S./M.E. patients produce an excess of lactate in their muscle cells during exercise and a lower VO_2 max (maximum volume of oxygen consumed) as compared with controls (see EXERCISE section earlier in this chapter). This could be as a consequence of :

1) predominantly anaerobic metabolism due to a preponderance of anaerobic as opposed to aerobic exercise or activity. (It is important when evaluating studies of C.F.S./M.E. and exercise to observe whether the exercise is aerobic or anaerobic) or

2) mild defects of **aerobic metabolism, oxidative phosphorylation** and **deficiency in pyruvate dehydrogenase** (as indicated in the Cell culture section

earlier in this chapter) that might result in anaerobic metabolism taking place by default.

It may be that graded aerobic exercise can stimulate self-repair mechanisms in the cell that correct the defects in aerobic metabolism. (Becoming so ill that they can only be mobile in a wheelchair may inadvertently 'lock' such C.F.S./M.E. sufferers into a lifestyle that excludes any possibility of aerobic exercise and therefore improvement).

My hypothesis is that during **anaerobic** activity (when largely **anaerobic metabolism** occurs) there is not enough energy produced to provide for the ATPase pump to return the lost K+ and for the anaerobic activity itself – such as sitting down, talking, pottering, cooking, standing, sitting reading and lecturing etc. resulting in fatigue.

Aerobic metabolism produces 13 times more energy than **anaerobic** metabolism. I suggest that only when a C.F.S./M.E. sufferer engages in **aerobic** activity (triggering **aerobic** metabolism) is there potentially enough energy produced for the K+ ATPase pump as well as the activity itself to occur without precipitating fatigue.

In describing the key C.F.S./M.E. symptom as "mild exercise causes disproportionate fatigue", I would say for me now at the stage I am at in the illness, this symptom is more accurately worded as "**anaerobic** activity causes disproportionate fatigue whilst **aerobic** exercise does not". Aerobic walking appears to increase subsequent anaerobic capacity. The question for research is to ask to what extent this applies to other C.F.S./M.E. sufferers.

It may be that the sustained **lack** of **aerobic** activity is where the problem lies for C.F.S./M.E. patients; and it may be just the loss of K+ ions particularly during anaerobic activity that cannot be tolerated in C.F.S./M.E. and is the major component in their fatigue.

I think 'pottering' is a disaster for C.F.S./M.E. sufferers. Such anaerobic activity whittles away at their energy producing little aerobic metabolism and energy (compared to healthy people) to replenish brain serotonin and potassium loss.

I have found that a period of aerobic walking before a period of anaerobic activity such as writing or interviewing a client, helps avoid early fatigue and results in more energy being available. For me aerobic walking generates greater **anaerobic** work capacity.

Some researchers working with C.F.S./M.E. patients, found that graded aerobic exercise did produce improvement in 50 per cent of the exercise treatment group compared to only 25 per cent improving in the flexibility exercise and relaxation treatment group. The positive effects were still apparent at the one year follow-up.

The aerobic exercise treatment group attended once a week for 12 weeks of supervised treatment. The flexibility and relaxation treatment group had the same treatment timetable.

I note that the two groups are in fact an aerobic group and an anaerobic group (i.e. the flexibility exercise and relaxation treatment group) but the authors do not emphasize the potential importance of this difference for C.F.S./M.E. sufferers. The grouping of the data in this study loses the individual differences in the effect of aerobic exercise. Even in the flexibility exercise and relaxation treatment group, 25 per cent improved.

This study does provide evidence for the benefits of aerobic exercise for C.F.S./M.E. patients.

It is paradoxical that aerobic exercise can not only be the cause of C.F.S./M.E. relapses, but also may have a major role in ameliorating the illness. For me a sufferer, the idea of the benefit of doing regular exercise, has come gradually, but still feels a dangerous activity. However, with the very gradual increase in aerobic activity (walking) my confidence has grown.

Using aerobic exercise as a therapy for C.F.S./M.E. is seemingly counter-intuitive. It is thinking the unthinkable, but if evidence continues to support it, it could be the lack of aerobic exercise that locks many sufferers into a life-time of the illness. Aerobic exercise may even have a role in the self-repair of cells, neurones and in brain plasticity. A full understanding and evaluation of the possible defects in aerobic and anaerobic metabolism occurring in C.F.S./M.E. is now necessary with a view to identifying patterns of effective management that could restore more energy to the sufferer.

Sources of fatigue in C.F.S./M.E. already identified are problems with:
1. Serotonin (5HT) receptors and cells }
2. acetylcholine receptors and cells } in the hypothalamus.
3. steroid receptors and cells }
4. potassium loss for cells
5. aerobic metabolism in cells
6. anxiety (and anticipatory fatigue)
7. lack of confidence in one's energy capacity
8. low regional cerebral blood flow
9. low grade continual infection
10. deconditioning (through too much inactivity)
11. hypoglycaemia (low blood glucose)
12. low blood volume
13. low blood pressure
14. stress
15. physical and emotional tension and
16. low estrogen in females

C.F.S./M.E. sufferers should avoid **stress** and **physical** and **emotional tension** as all three will deplete serotonin and increase loss of potassium, contributing to unnecessary fatigue.

If neurones in the hypothalamus region of the brain where the emotions are controlled, have been affected by viral infection, damaged and are losing potassium, then strong emotions positive or negative will not only deplete serotonin the main neurotransmitter in this region but also run down potassium as these neurones are activated. Meditation in which the mind stills both thinking and emotions, will rest these neurones and allow replenishment of the cell serotonin and potassium.

However, too much rest will restore potassium but may, depending on how well the sufferer is, conserve serotonin to such an extent that sleep onset at bedtime is delayed.

Treatment effect of aerobic activity

The two main defects in C.F.S./M.E. may be the damaged serotonin receptors and the abnormal potassium loss. Above all the sufferer must apply this knowledge of aerobic and anaerobic activity, brain neurotransmitters like serotonin and loss of potassium in conjunction with good self-knowledge and self-awareness in an intelligent way. Aerobic exercise is a high-risk strategy as wrongly applied at the wrong time it could cause a major setback or relapse.

Aerobic activity oxygenates the blood and thereby the brain and body. It causes an increase in mitochondria in cells. With more mitochondria available for energy production, C.F.S./M.E. fatigue may diminish; a self-repairing process.

Similarly, gradually increasing mental activity, (which causes an increase in blood flow in the brain and the number of cell mitochondria, - again aiding the production of cell energy), might be expected to ameliorate the serotonin, acetylcholine, norepinephrine, vasopressin and steroid receptor damage found in the brains of C.F.S./M.E. patients described by Chaudhuri, Behan and Behan (1998).

Eating foods rich in potassium like bananas may help.

Some C.F.S./M.E. patients are known to inadvertently hyperventilate causing themselves some distressing symptoms. This might be as a result of the body's attempt to oxygenate the blood and brain, better done by aerobic activity.

Timing of aerobic activity
If the sufferer has slept normally, then serotonin levels are likely to be at their highest in the morning. Consequently fatigue felt at this time is likely to be due to loss of potassium and hence graded aerobic exercise like walking may resolve it. Anaerobic activity like deskwork lowers potassium levels, whilst aerobic exercise or rest returns them to the cells.
However, fatigue later in the day is likely to be due to both lowered serotonin levels and K^+ loss. Aerobic exercise at this point is not recommended as both might be lowered further. Rest is suggested at this point to resolve fatigue.

A long stretch of anaerobic activity like driving or talking over a meal, depletes levels of neurotransmitter chemicals in the brain, and cell potassium. Aerobic activity at this time will probably only result in further fatigue; running these chemicals to even lower levels.

Aerobic activity (walking) just **before** an anticipated period of anaerobic activity seems to increase the length of time the latter can be coped with successfully.

Aerobic exercise may only be therapeutic after a degree of recovery (possibly of the serotonin receptors and cells in the hypothalamus) has already occurred and may exacerbate the fatigue if undertaken too early in the recovery process of the illness.

When resting and recovering from activity, I can feel a tingling in the muscles which may be potassium levels being restored in neurones and muscle cells.

Rules

Each sufferer could create their own aerobic exercise rules in conjunction with planned aerobic and anaerobic activity. E.g. my rules are:

a) Do aerobic activity in the morning (when serotonin levels are likely to be high) before any protracted period of anaerobic activity. The reverse is to be avoided.

b) Avoid excessively long periods of anaerobic activity; punctuate it with aerobic exercise like walking.

c) Avoid too much aerobic activity at the end of the day when serotonin is naturally running down.

d) Initially very gradually build up both aerobic and anaerobic activities separately, starting from as little as a few seconds or minutes at first.

e) To timetable the aerobic and anaerobic activity optimally with other events in the day.

f) To avoid too much aerobic activity as it may cause bursts of anxiety. It is possible that low blood glucose (hypoglycaemia) caused by the exertion results in adrenaline being released as part of the body's attempt to produce more glucose from the muscles to raise blood glucose. Sometimes the brain interprets the presence of adrenaline in the bloodstream as anxiety. Eating carbohydrate in my experience can resolve such symptoms.

g) To avoid all activity if ill or fatigued and thereafter build the length of the activity again very gradually.

h) To avoid punishing oneself for lapses in self-management. Just try to learn something from the event to improve the success of future management.

i) To develop a safe routine that can be coped with enjoyably, in work and holiday periods.

Research is needed to evaluate the generalisability of these ideas.

<u>Personal examples</u>
Having generated a theory or hypothesis it is possible to try to test its veracity by endeavouring to explain personal instances of illness or fatigue using it.

I discovered the effect of aerobic exercise accidently, through personal awareness and reading about the potassium loss from neurones. I could easily have missed the significance of aerobic activity. For a long time I have learnt to avoid energetic activity; trapping myself at this point in the illness. One wonders how many other sufferers are locked into this 'self-trap'.

Aerobic exercise (walking) first thing each morning and afternoon, appears to boost my energy enough to make coping with subsequent anaerobic activity like sedentary work, typing, reading or writing more easy. In a routine morning I walk for 45 minutes, then type for 45, rest lying down meditating for 15 minutes plus a mug of filtered water, then do 40 step-ups and then back to typing for 45 minutes and repeat the cycle until lunch time at 12-30 pm.

After lunch and resting for an hour, I repeat the process in the afternoon starting with a walk of between 30 – 45 minutes.

This regime has enabled me to double the amount of anaerobic sedentary work I can achieve in a day from about 2.5 hours to 5 hours per day.

Because I can only jog comfortably for 60 seconds before discomfort in the leg muscles occurs, I am experimenting with periods of gentle walking between one minute jogging episodes. The aim always is to enjoy the exercise whilst avoiding discomfort or pain. The energizing effects of aerobic walking can last for up to two hours, so it is not recommended just before going to bed as it prevents sleep.

Since 1987 until recently I've mistakenly avoided aerobic exercise; for example stopping playing table tennis after a minute or two as soon as I start breathing heavily. Sufferers need to identify the safest, most effective daily ratio of aerobic to anaerobic activity for themselves; a personal ratio A/AN. For me to be at my most productive the ratio is 1.5/5.5 hours up to 3/7 hours. This means that if I walk for a total of 1.5 hours a day in two or three outings, I can achieve 5.5 hours of sedentary work, but if I can do 3 hours a day comfortably and enjoyably I can achieve 7 hours sedentary work. This has been achieved by very gradual increases over 10 years. However, on holiday I have done 4 hours walking in a day but only 6 hours of sedentary work, showing that there is a limit to the benefit of aerobic exercise, for me.

I can see now that trying to remain in my full-time employment, (which involved eight or nine hours of anaerobic activities like driving, sedentary work, interviewing, reading and thinking) eventually led to multiple relapses and early retirement. Knowing what I now know about interspersing aerobic exercise like walking with anaerobic activity and working part-time I might have avoided having to give up my career.

A classic change in my management of myself since discovering the research on potassium loss and aerobic exercise has been from **resting** for 30-45 minutes before seeing a client for the morning in my work as a private psychologist – to going for a **walk** for 30 minutes before, instead. This has resulted in less fatigue in the afternoon after seeing a client.

In July '99 I did a 35 minute aerobic walk and then 230 minutes of anaerobic activity and felt well. But a further 15 minutes reading resulted in 1½ hours of very unpleasant fatigue. It may be that too much anaerobic activity seriously depletes potassium ions and serotonin in C.F.S./M.E. By observing the symptoms of the fatigue the sufferer might be able to identify which is the cause. Depleted serotonin may result in symptoms of a dysfunctional hypothalamus (see the list the symptoms that suggest hypothalamic involvement in C.F.S./M.E. in the earlier section HYPOTHALAMIC DYSFUNCTION IN C.F.S./M.E. in this chapter).

Another day's experience is yet more evidence for the amazing value of aerobic exercise (walking). On Sunday 8 August '99, my wife Susan and I, had driven, towing our caravan, the one hour journey from Azay-le-Rideau to Civray de Touraine near to the Chateau of Chenonceau in France, arriving at 12 noon. After lunch I rested for an hour. The afternoon was spent in the Orangery terrace at the chateau drinking coffee because of the rain. Becoming chilled we returned to the caravan at 4pm and I rested again. By 7-30pm I felt exhausted. Why? I wasn't sure. I had not done more than usual. It might have been the earlier chilling or lack of any aerobic exercise that day.

However, Susan persuaded me to go for a walk. Suspicious and lacking confidence, I agreed as long as we could stop as soon as I felt worse. We set off and over the next 45 minutes I did not get any worse but gradually began to feel better. Muscles lost their wobbly feeling. I resisted a number of panic attacks as my confidence waned and I imagined being set back. At the end of the walk I felt supersonic – revitalized with energy. I could scarcely believe it.

A year or so earlier, feeling that exhausted at 7-30pm I would have rested all evening and the next day. This time I judged that my serotonin level could not be too low and not the cause of the fatigue, but rather that the fatigue was due to a day of too much anaerobic activity (driving, ambling, resting and sitting down most of the afternoon).

I considered that I had probably lost too much potassium from neurones and I did not have the energy to pump them back. The oxygen from the aerobic walk had, I suggest, allowed aerobic metabolism to take place providing much more energy than anaerobic metabolism.

But to go for a walk when one feels fatigued is counter-intuitive. Because it is unthinkable, one could imagine being trapped into a lifestyle that specifically excludes a potential healing force; aerobic exercise.

It is a morning of unbroken anaerobic activity with no walking at all that exhausts me for the afternoon and evening. I now avoid sustained **anaerobic** activity and the debilitating episode of symptoms that follow it, that have the effect of lowering self-confidence and self-efficacy. Periods of anaerobic activity need to be broken up into smaller periods.

The most demanding and exhausting of anaerobic activity, in my experience is standing still and social interaction. The more people that one interacts with at home or at work, then the more talking, thinking and emotional expression are required. Paradoxically even the pleasure and excitement of socializing, is tiring. Having friends to stay for the weekend is an example of this. Talking needs to be rationed and managed like any other activity that a C.F.S./M.E. sufferer undertakes, if they are to remain well.

Reducing the dose of the tranquillizer, perphenazine, that I had been prescribed, resulted in lowered energy levels for several months. This may be due to more neurones (nerve fibres) firing because fewer receptors are blocked due to less tranquillizer. The more neurones that fire, the more serotonin is released and the more opportunities for potassium loss there are; both resulting in depletion of each substance producing the effect of fatigue. The answer seemed to be to wait for the neurones to stablize and also to be as relaxed as possible in all activities in order to keep the number of neurones firing to a minimum.

My endeavour each day is to judiciously alternate aerobic walking, sedentary work, with rest, regular food and intermittent social interaction in order to be happiest and most productive.

Research might work towards the aim of explaining the biochemical and cellular activities that are associated with each C.F.S./M.E. symptom and devising self-management strategies of input and output to ameliorate them.

Further evaluation of aerobic exercise is required to discover its treatment generalisability for C.F.S./M.E.

Conclusion
These two **principal** causes of fatigue in C.F.S./M.E. in my view, low levels of secretion of serotonin in the brain and loss of potassium, may mark different stages of development and recovery in the illness. Both probably are occurring together, but it may be only when serotonin production has recovered somewhat, to allow some sort of activity, will the difference in response to aerobic compared to anaerobic activity showing a possible potassium loss problem, be noticably apparent.

Stress, excitement, anxiety, tension, speeding (i.e. rushing) etc. all are likely to create muscle tension which will unproductively activate neurones and muscle cells unnecessarily consuming energy. This, and the energy lost through the restoration of potassium levels will lead to premature fatigue.

These activities should be avoided by C.F.S./M.E. sufferers. Relaxation whilst being active, and using only the muscles necessary for the execution of the activity, again are likely to save energy.

Meditation, relaxation and sleep are ways of replenishing the brain neurotransmitter serotonin and potassium ions.

It requires much self-management skill to keep this balance between aerobic, anaerobic activity and rest, especially when the C.F.S./M.E. sufferer can be open to disruptive events from surprising sources. Recently seeing a film with a very sad ending 'House of Mirth' and doing badly in a quiz night for me, resulted in two bouts of depressed mood lasting a few days. The concomitant negative feelings, precluded conformity to optimal self-management strategies, making the setback worse.

SELF-MANAGEMENT OF BIOLOGICAL FUNCTIONS

The aspects of input and output of living that a sufferer has under their control are (for input) the use of the five senses (vision, hearing, touch, smell and taste), drinking, eating, breathing, and (for output) socializing, talking, mental and physical activity.

For the input, drinking clean filtered or bottled water, getting fresh air and eating food that is free from pesticides can be organised and will promote good health, but so too will gradually increasing the output of mental and physical activity. Some researchers contend that adequate blood flow to the brain and body is a factor in natural healing and both mental and physical activity promote good blood flow.

Such physical and mental activity, gradually, sensibly and pleasurable increased in small steps may offer a method of promoting self-repair in cells of the brain (brain plasticity) and the body.

Evidence for this comes from the finding that activity generates not only the firing of neurones but also, following the stimulation of the post-synaptic receptors, the second messenger systems involving molecules like cAMP (cyclic Adenosine Mono Phosphate) to trigger the cell nucleus to generate protein for:

1. maintaining the structure of the cell
2. enzymes for the internal functioning of the cell and
3. producing new receptors and messenger molecules;

all of which are aspects of self-repair and maintenance of cells.

The second messenger system may be involved in C.F.S./M.E.

An individual can alter and manage their own brain chemistry in various ways.

a) Life-changing stress with poor coping causes an increase in corticocosteroids and the suppression of the immune system. Better coping or avoidance of the stress, would reverse this.

b) Stress causes a decrease in the functioning of interleukin (IL-2R) receptors. Better coping would reverse this and improve the immune system for fighting infection.

c) Rewards and rewarding events (maybe even self-reward and love) cause a cascade of the brain neurotransmitter chemicals, serotonin, enkephalin, GABA (Gamma Amino Butyric Acid) and then dopamine. Each little praising comment and every compliment causes a reward cascade of pleasure. Thinking pleasant memories is likely to also trigger a reward cascade, changing brain chemistry and changing one's mood; (with the reverse [punishment and criticism] generating stress responses).

d) Sensory stimulation causes ACTH (adrenocorticotrophic hormone also called adrenocorticotrophin or corticotrophin) to flow, stimulating epinephrine, that then triggers the release of vasopressin, then enkephalins and then endorphins resulting in feelings of pleasure.

(ACTH is a hormone synthesized and stored in the anterior pituitary gland, large amounts of which are released in response to any form of stress. ACTH controls the secretion of corticosteroid hormones [cortisol or referred to as hydrocortisone, the major glucocorticoid] from the adrenal gland of the kidneys).

258

e) Feelings of love, happiness, touch, massage, relaxation, laughing and meditation all cause a decrease in stress hormones like ACTH and increase endorphins which make people feel happier.

Feelings of love also increase the antibody IgA immunoglobulin generated by B lymphocytes (immune cells) in the blood which combat cold and flu viruses.

f) Exposure to sunshine, eating carbohydrate, eating fats (not recommended in excess), smoking cigarettes (not recommended), aerobic exercise etc. all cause an increase in serotonin release.

g) Alcohol comsumption causes a decrease in serotonin levels in the brain.

h) The emotion of fear, threat or stress maintained for 60 minutes produces feelings of energy causing an increase in serotonin and norepinephrine which then cause an increase in the activity of the sympathetic nervous system. This causes an increase in adrenaline and corticosteroid hormones [cortisol or referred to as hydrocortisone the major glucocorticoid] from the adrenal gland of the kidneys. This is required for normal carbohydrate metabolism, but is also a response to any stress. Most intermittent stress of short duration is good for the body and mind. It is prolonged stress and lack of perceived control over it that generates the damaging effects of strain. Relaxation for 20 minutes restores equilibrium.

i) If the individual's self-esteem (how he feels about himself) is raised this causes an increase in vaso-intestinal polypeptide (VIP) which then causes an increase in lymphocyte function and this enhances the immune system response.

j) The first 90 minutes of sleep cause an increase in growth hormone (GH, or referred to as somatotrophin – a hormone synthesized and stored in the anterior pituitary gland. It promotes growth of the long bones in the limbs, increases protein synthesis and is necessary in the body's response to exercise, hypoglycaemia, sleep, hunger, starvation etc.). It has been found that steroid receptor damage in C.F.S./M.E. patients and those exposed to organo-phosphates pesticides, causes a below normal output of growth hormone from the anterior pituitary gland. Increased levels of growth hormone cause an increase in the body's healing responses.

k) **Chronic stress** can give rise to **addictions** via, excess adrenaline and cortisol causing:
    1). Receptors to be flooded, causing
    2). receptor damage i.e. down regulation causing
    3). withdrawal feelings and then the individual
    4). overworks to try to compensate.

l) Challenge gives rise to an increase in catecholamines e.g.epinephrine (also called adrenaline) and norepinephrine (also called noradrenaline).

m) Coping gives rise to a decrease in epinephrine (adrenaline) and norepinephrine (noradrenaline).

n) Cathartic psychotherapy followed by emotional insight involves an increase in ACTH causing an increase in cortisol which increases endorphins giving feelings of satisfaction.

o) Endorphins block pain transmission. 'Substance P' facilitates pain transmission.

p) Eating well increases gastrointestinal (GI) tract cholecystokinin which in the brain aids memory.

q) Irritability is often due to low serotonin. It particularly afflicts old people.

r) Emotional stress decreases self-repair by cells and the avoidance of emotional stress plus relaxation will promote DNA self-repair following viral damage. Negative emotions increase muscle tension and activate the sympathetic nervous system. Neurones and muscle cells activated in this way for long periods will result in continued loss of potassium from ion channel in the C.F.S./M.E. patient, resulting in unnecessary fatigue.

s) Exposure to sunlight generates serotonin in the brain.

t) Aerobic exercise stimulates oxygenation of the blood, brain and body, production of serotonin and psychological well-being.

u) Eating carbohydrate (a sandwich) 20 minutes before going to bed stimulates production of acetylcholine (at a time when serotonin is falling) in the brain and this promotes sleep.

v) Reading before bedtime helps reduce serotonin in the brain resulting in the ascendancy of acetylcholine and this promotes sleep.

w) Sleep onset should be about 20 minutes after retiring to bed; longer means the individual has done too little activity during the day; shorter means that they have done too much.

x) Having a hot drink causes a release of endorphins in the brain and lifts the mood.

PATHWAYS FOR FUTURE RESEARCH

Chaudhuri, Behan & Behan (1998) conclude that altered synaptic sensitivities to acetylcholine and serotonin with secondary changes at other receptors, such as glucocorticoid, may explain many symptoms in C.F.S./M.E.

It has been postulated that C.F.S./M.E. may be caused by viral injury to **muscle** cell ion channels. Indeed, viruses and toxins appear to be the two commonest precipitants of C.F.S./M.E.

It is thus possible that membrane-associated receptor dysfunction resulting in potassium ion loss, is the primary dysfunction in C.F.S./M.E. and chronic organophosphate-exposed individuals and their neuroendocrine abnormalities are secondary to it according to Chaudhuri, Behan & Behan (1998).

OVERALL CONCLUSION

Risk factors for C.F.S. following a viral illness are, previous history of fatigue, psychiatric illness, belief in vulnerability to viruses and having poor health before the viral illness. Women are more likely to develop C.F.S./M.E. than men.

Chaudhuri, Behan & Behan (1998) in their paper have identified a number of different possible **causes** of C.F.S./M.E. :

1. viral infection,
2. emotional or physical trauma,
3. immunisation,
4. ciguatera fish poisoning,
5. food poisoning - botulism,
6. organo-phosphate and carbamate pesticides,
7. sick building syndrome,
8. stress,
9. severe physical exercise,
10. multiple chemical sensitivity,
11. silicone breast implants in women,
12. organochlorines (hexachlorobenzene - HCB),
13. chronic lead poisoning,

14. polio.
15. low estrogen levels in women.

I would suggest that these categories could be seem as a possible subclassification of C.F.S./M.E. and may require different treatments.

In summary the **medical anomalies** found in C.F.S./M.E. are (see the earlier part of this chapter for a fuller explanation):

Immunology
- Up or down regulated immune system
- Atopy (a form of allergy)

Abnormal laboratory findings
- re: blood cells, reduced intracellular carnitine and other anomalies (see Table 3.2)

Genetics
- Mitochondrial DNA damage

Muscles
- Reduction in the exercise capacity, excessively early intracellular acidification, both increased acidification relative to phosphocreatine (PCr) depletion and reduced acidification. A significant reduction in **aerobic** metabolism was noted in PCr recovery. Reduced oxidative muscle metabolism. The oxidative capacity (maximal rate of Adenosine Triphosphate [ATP] synthesis) is significantly reduced.
- mild defects of **aerobic metabolism,** defect in **oxidative phosphorylation,** mild **deficiency in pyruvate dehydrogenase.**

Exercise

- C.F.S./M.E. patients showed a lower VO_2 max (maximum volume of oxygen consumed), abnormal lactate response and above normal heart rate, a markedly rapid decline in quadriceps tension was evident in the patient group at 200 minutes (3 hours 20 minutes) and on the following day (after 24 hours) during recovery.

Other findings

- Low blood pressure
- low level of blood flow in the brain (rCBF)
- hypothalamic dysfunction
- Up regulated serotonin receptors
- Up regulated acetylcholine receptors
- Down regulated norepinephrine receptors
- Down regulated glucocorticoid receptors
- Down regulated vasopressin receptors
- abnormal hypothalamic arginine-vasopressin secretion and water metabolism in C.F.S./M.E. patients
- Malfunctioning mitochondria
- Resting energy expenditure (REE) raised
- Myocarditis (acute or chronic inflammation of the heart muscle)
- change in cell metabolism resulting from abnormal potassium ion loss from ion channels of cells. It is thus possible that membrane-associated receptor dysfunction is the primary dysfunction in C.F.S./M.E.
- low estrogen levels in some female C.F.S./M.E. patients.

Some affected cells may have multiple biochemical dysfunctions of those listed above.

Fatigue appears to be **improved** during pregnancy but there is often severe 'rebound fatigue' in the period after childbirth. Fatigue is **worsened** during menstruation, by a heavy meal, a prolonged hot bath or alcohol.

A summary of the **predictors of outcome** once ill with C.F.S./M.E. are as follows:

A **poor** outcome is likely if there is ongoing evidence of immune activation, chronic viral infection, current emotional disorder, strength of attribution of illness to physical causes (i.e. believing that most illness has a physical cause only), a primary psychiatric diagnosis and a defensive (suppressive) coping style.

A **good outcome** appears to be more likely when the sufferer, does not have a strong conviction in a physical disease process and is open to the possibility of psychological and social factors being involved in the course of the illness;   expresses their emotions openly rather than as somatization (physical symptoms) or suppresses their feelings altogether; does not have a defensive style of coping; is free from on-going infection and is without major emotional disorders. Only 5% of C.F.S./M.E. cases report no current symptoms.

Treatment
Chaudhuri, Behan and Behan (1998) conclude that treatment in C.F.S./M.E. has so far been symptomatic, mainly directed to the relief of painful symptoms, sleep problems and the associated mild depression. Treatment of fatigue in C.F.S./M.E. has largely been unsuccessful and no sustained benefit was observed from the use of a number of agents in open-labelled trials. These included corticosteroids, mineralocorticoid (fludrocortisone), amantadine and 3, 4 diaminopyridine. No improvement occurred in most of Chaudhuri, Behan and Behan's (1998) patients treated with nutritional supplements such as essential fatty acids, coenzyme Q10 carnitine and choline. They also used anti-epileptic drugs like

carbamazepine,lamotrigine and phenytoin, which are effective for pain relief and suppressing ephaptic (brain waves) neuronal activation that occcurs in neuralgias (severe burning or stabbing pain that often follows the course of a nerve). Patients treated with carbamazepine did experience a partial reduction of fatigue and so did a few patients on lamotrigine. Except for occasional patients with fibromyalgia and C.F.S./M.E. who responded to low-dose amitriptyline, use of antidepressants (both monoamine reuptake inhibitor and selective serotonin reuptake inhibitor [SSRI] groups of drugs) in any dose range, failed to improve the central symptom of fatigue in most patients. However, overall, such patients experienced less frequent mood swings while taking one of the selective SSRIs, sertraline, or one of the newer antidepressants, venlafaxine. (I when on 150mgs of amitriptyline a day was able to work full-time with no symptoms, but through overwork completely relapsed and had to retire early).

Chaudhuri, Behan and Behan (1998) found in their research that there was no sustained improvement of fatigue with the use of central stimulants (nicotine transdermal patches and methylphenidate, alone or in combination).

Though Chaudhuri, Behan and Behan (1998) say they have had no experience in the use of immune system modifiers, they report that several agents of this class have been tried by other workers but there is no evidence at present that any of these agents (e.g. human immunoglobulin, ampligen) is effective in ameliorating fatigue symptoms. Other treatments tried unsuccessfully in C.F.S./M.E. include beta blockers (e.g. atenolol), calcium channel blockers (e.g. nimodipine), opiate antagonists (naltrexone), antivirals (acyclovir), melatonin and magnesium. **Oestrogen therapy** has recently been claimed to improve symptoms in perimenopausal (around the time of the menopause when women stop producing egg cells) women with syndrome X, and also with C.F.S.

Researchers looking for a single treatment for C.F.S./M.E. could be mistaken and a single treatment identified as effective for

C.F.S./M.E. by properly controlled trials is not the same as an individually designed treatment programme consisting of a variety of different components, of proven effectiveness, for a particular patient and agreed by him/her. In fact what is needed ideally is a programme of properly controlled trials of the latter using appropriate single-case experimental designs.

As can be seen, many treatments for C.F.S./M.E. are only partially effective or not at all. The sufferer must capitalize on all the treatment factors that may have any small positive effect, namely;

- Some sufferers are helped by antidepressant medication (e.g. amitriptyline),

- Taking time to have a breakfast of, for example, whole grain cereal is associated with less heart disease, diabetes and obesity. Having breakfast would help chronically ill people avoid other potential illnesses.

- drinking large quantities of filtered **water** will help bulk up low blood volume and wash out pollutants, but too much must be avoided as valuable salts and minerals can be eliminated,

- consuming adequate **salt** will maintain blood pressure and could ameliorate potassium loss from cells, thereby reducing the associated fatigue,

- eating enough **carbohydrate** regularly will maintain blood glucose and avoid hypoglycaemia. (Eat **organic food** where possible to **avoid pesticides**),

- eating a balanced diet and being aware of the following types of food;

- Cancer fighting foods are: broccoli, spinach, tomatoes, oranges.

267

- <u>Heart protection</u> foods are salmon, walnuts, soya.

- <u>Cholesterol lowering</u> foods are: beans, oats, blueberries, prunes, apple juice.

- <u>Immune system supporting</u> foods are: yogurt, turkey.

- <u>Antidepressant foods</u> are: meat, liver, pumpkin seeds, brewers' yeast providing the mineral zinc; liver, egg yolk, wholemeal bread, shellfish, prunes providing iron; nuts, shrimps, winkles, soya, leafy green vegetables, grapes, dates, oats, figs, ginger, bananas, hummus, nutmeg providing magnesium.

- to improve cerebral blood flow (**Ginkgo Biloba** may help – Murray (1996) and some physical activity every hour no matter how small; i.e. a walk round the house for 5 minutes; this will also help avoid venous pooling of stale blood, low blood pressure and the consequent associated fatigue,

- since some research suggests that there is cell wall damage in C.F.S./M.E. then taking the food supplements Lecithin (from www.HollandandBarrett.com) and phosphatidyl serine (called Memo Plus from www.Healthspan.co.uk) should be evaluated as they are the natural molecules used by the body to create cell walls and membranes.

- **Evening primrose oil** (or Efamol oil) has helped some C.F.S./M.E. sufferers,

- **Magnesium sulphate injections** have helped some sufferers,

- **Iron supplements** have been found to reduce persistent fatigue felt by healthy people who show problems with **ferritin** (an iron-protein complex that is one of the forms in which iron is stored in the tissues) according to a blood test.

- **Organo-phosphate pesticides** cause incomplete digestion of some foods resulting in excess opiod molecules in the bloodstream. There is evidence that a **wheat-free (gluten-free)** and **dairy products-free** diet is beneficial to C.F.S./M.E. sufferers.(See website; http://osiris.sunderland.ac.uk/autism/)

- See www.pesticidescampaign.co.uk for more about the link between pesticides and chronic illness.

- **Vitamin B complex** can alleviate anxiety.

- Recent research has found that the food supplement compounds, **alpha lipoic acid** (an antioxidant which combats free radical molecules that cause ageing) and **acetyl L carnitine** can reverse the ageing process and it is suggested that they may therefore indirectly help C.F.S./M.E. Acetyl L carnitine takes fat into cells to burn to produce energy in the mitochondria for cell self-repair and all cell functions. Both compounds are available from health food shops like Holland and Barrett.

- Look at Dr. Perrin's work at www.theperrinclinic.com He suggests that **massage** can help recover from C.F.S./M.E.

- **Healthy beliefs**; are 1) not having a strong conviction in a physical disease process and 2) open to the possibility of psychological and social factors being involved in the course of the illness; 3) expressing your emotions overtly,

- avoid getting **cold or chilled**; I have found this very fatiguing and it can take weeks from which to recover,

- having realistic daily and hourly **goals**,

- **peace of mind** and,

- **resting, relaxation, meditation; hypnotherapy** can resolve anxiety,

- Some researchers believe that **meditation** may increase serotonin levels in the brain generating a calming effect. Others suggest that **meditation** can improve happiness (Sunday Times, p14, 14-5-03).

- gradually increasing **aerobic, anaerobic physical** and **mental activity;** I attribute some of my recovery to the therapeutic effect provided by the goal of writing this book,

- **avoid stress** (i.e. rushing about, being tense, speeding when doing any activity. This consumes energy unnecessarily). Better recovery is likely if the sufferer ceases all stressful activity, like extra tasks at work or at home immediately C.F.S./M.E. is diagnosed or suspected, and resumed only gradually when a complete recovery is apparent. The sufferer should definitely not struggle on trying to cope.

- **music**,

- **changing your mood with your mind.** This can be done by, listening to uplifting music, watching a happy film or comedy, or reading positive quotations, in the Bible or Koran or novel etc.

  Similarly a low mood can be generated or exacerbated by exposure to sad music, film or reading material.

If <u>bereaved</u> avoid sad music, films or reading material and seek out the opposite. Make a list of positive uplifting statements and quotations. In fact set up a daily and weekly timetable of happy, positive experiences.

- **natural healing** (Rossi, 1993; Benson & Stark, 1996),

- **religion and prayer** (Hirshberg & Barasch, 1995; Dossey, 1995),

- having a spiritual life (**spirituality;** Swinton, 2001),

- wholesome **pleasure** (Blum, 1996) and happiness from a loving relationship(s), work and leisure activities (Argyle, 1993),

- **humour and laughter,**

- **Cognitive Behaviour Therapy or Counseling**, (Trower <u>et al</u>. 1988)

- **self-reward** and **avoidance of self-punishment,**

- **self-help groups**,

- **conversation** on topics of particular personal interest, (Gilligan & Price (1993),

- **dancing** (Freeman, 1995),

- **self-management** and **self efficacy** (the **beliefs** that one's behaviour can positively affect the course of C.F.S./M.E. and that one can achieve the goals one has set oneself, are necessary. It is **erroneous beliefs** about C.F.S./M.E. which can maintain the sufferer in the illness; in a self-trap). The Chronic Fatigue Syndrome Unit at King's

College Hospital London (tel: 0207-346-3363) has a very useful website www.kcl.ac.uk/cfs on which is published their rehabilitation programme involving self-management for C.F.S./M.E. This is a very welcome and significant development. The details are available to download. Lorig (1999) and Lorig & Fries (2000) describe other self-management programmes.

- Exposure to pictures of **nature** or nature itself – like parks, countryside, forests, mountains etc can lower stress levels and lead to general health improvement. See research by Roger Ulrich.

- **Friendship** and

- **Community** (being part of a community, church, club, association or any group that meet together regularly) can provide unique pleasure that promotes healing.

- Very gradual return to as normal a life as possible, avoiding fatigue by knowing the limits. The sufferer needs a safe sustainable initial skeleton schedule or timetable of daily activities or events to build on; starting with getting up in the morning at no later than 9 a.m., washing and dressing with rest interspersed as necessary. As the sufferer improves, as shown by a daily diary record, more events can be added. Events should be interspersed with rewards, e.g. a cup of tea, a short phone-call to a friend or relative, five minutes of a game of chess, fifteen minutes read etc. If an unavoidable stress occurs (a relative becomes ill) then rest more and do less of something else whilst the stress persists. Be kind to yourself.

- In retrospect a factor of enormous importance in helping many couples, get through the illness, is the practice of frequently, many times a day, asking each other and telling each other how they were feeling. Constantly monitoring and communicating their state of mind and health to each other avoids damaging misunderstanding from developing.

The Most Important Advice
Of all the advice on the management of C.F.S./M.E. the following are probably the most important.

1. Good self-management and the avoidance of "pushing oneself".
2. Follow Dr. Charles Shepherd's 10 steps for effective management (see below).
3. Follow a programme of very very gradually increasing graded exercise.
4. Use of cognitive behavioural counselling (Trower et al. 1988) to learn the most effective beliefs and attitudes to hold about C.F.S./M.E. (www.Ultrasis.com are trialing a computerized version of cognitive behavioural counselling that does not require a counsellor or psychologist. It could be available soon for people to use in their own home).
5. Take Efamol, evening primrose oil and fish oils.
6. Gluten free diet (see website (http://osiris.sunderland.ac.uk/autism/).
7. Meet other C.F.S./M.E. sufferers; attend a C.F.S./M.E. local group.
8. Have a safe sustainable daily routine.

Dr. Charles Shepherd of the M.E. Association recommends following 10 important aspects of the self-management of C.F.S./M.E.

1 Make sure the diagnosis is correct
He says that it is not always easy for a doctor to make a decision as to when a period of post-viral debility is turning into something more serious (i.e. C.F.S./M.E.). However, a diagnosis of C.F.S./M.E. should certainly be considered when flu-like

symptoms, along with the characteristic muscle fatigue, sleep disturbance, and cognitive dysfunction (i.e. problems with memory, concentration), persist for more than four to six weeks after an acute infection or some other triggering event. Any GP should be capable of making a presumptive diagnosis of C.F.S./M.E. at this stage - provided there are no other indications from the patient's history which suggest that there could be an alternative explanation.

2 Consultant referral

Shepherd (2001) says that most people with C.F.S./M.E. can and should be managed by their general practitioner and members of the primary healthcare team. However, if there is a query over diagnosis, or uncertainties about management, then referral to a hospital specialist for a second opinion should be speedily arranged. Unfortunately, the situation in many parts of the UK is that no such specialists are available and referral outside a health authority boundary can involve difficulties. He says that everyone who is severely affected should be assessed at least once by a specialist with expertise in the illness and preferably be under the joint care of both a hospital specialist and their GP. All children who are sufficiently unwell to be away from school for more than three months should be under the joint care of a hospital or community paediatrician and their GP.

3 Activity management

Achieving the correct balance between activity and rest is the most important aspect of lifestyle management. In practice, this will involve an individual management programme which is based on the stage and severity of the condition. Shepherd (2001) believes that the best form of activity management is a procedure known as pacing - something which is described in more detail in the Question and Answer section of this issue. He does not believe that graded exercise programmes which encourage a much more progressive and far less flexible approach to increasing levels of aerobic activity are helpful or appropriate.

4 Drug treatments

At present, he continues, there is no drug treatment that can successfully treat or cure the underlying illness. A number of drugs have shown some benefits in clinical trials (e.g. very low doses of hydrocortisone) but their use remains experimental. There are, however, a number of drugs which can provide relief from specific symptoms (eg a low dose of amitriptyline at night for muscle pain and/or sleep disturbance).

5 Emotional and psychiatric problems

As with any other chronic illness, people with C.F.S./M.E. may go on to develop emotional and psychiatric problems. If this happens, Shepherd suggests talking to the GP and taking advantage of whatever help is appropriate. True clinical depression -as opposed to just feeling 'fed up' about the illness -requires treatment with antidepressants. Cognitive behaviour therapy (CBT), which is not always administered in a psychiatric setting, can sometimes be helpful for those who are finding it difficult to cope with self-help management of their illness.

6 Work, education and family responsibilities

Most people with C.F.S./M.E., especially during the very early stages, will find that they are no longer able to carry on with their normal work, education or domestic responsibilities. If this is the case, then it is vital that they stay in touch with a key person at work (i.e. personnel manager, occupational health doctor) to let them know how they are progressing. The same applies to a child or young person at school or college. As time goes on, the sufferer may be fortunate and find themselves in a position where some form of limited return to work or education becomes possible. For others, the outcome is far less satisfactory, and permanent retirement on grounds of permanent ill health may need to be considered (see special feature in the Welfare section of this issue, p12). It should be noted that C.F.S./M.E. is an illness that is covered by the Disability Discrimination Act. The Act provides important legal protection when it comes to decisions about adaptions and changes in working hours/practice which may need to be made at work as well as protection from dismissal on grounds of ill health (Shepherd, 2001).

7 Benefits

People with C.F.S./M.E. are entitled to claim a range of state sickness and disability benefits although the process of doing so often involves a number of very unfair hurdles.

For those unable to work, the current incapacity benefit (ICB) eligibility criteria is a far from ideal way of assessing someone's ability to work. In an illness like C.F.S./M.E., the ability to carry out tasks such as lifting objects or walking up stairs rapidly declines as the task is repeated, and no satisfactory allowance for this aspect of the illness is made for in the official assessments. Consequently, obtaining ICB often has more to do with the way the forms are filled in than the real level of disability. High levels of success on appeal also confirm the unsatisfactory way in which people with C.F.S./M.E. are currently being assessed. Anyone who is more severely affected from the point of view of mobility and/or personal care requirements should apply for a Disability Living Allowance.

8 Social support and practical assistance

More severely affected people with C.F.S./M.E. may be entitled to various forms of practical assistance such as a wheelchair or practical social support in the form of a home help. For advice and information on practical aids for the disabled, contact the nearest Disabled Living Centre. Local authority social services departments should be able to advise on home helps and agencies who may be able to put you in touch with volunteers. A growing number of GP surgeries now employ professional counsellors who are often a good source of additional information on organisations worth approaching for help (Shepherd, 2001).

9 Carers

Although it is very easy to start losing contact with friends, relatives and work colleagues if you have an illness like C.F.S./M.E., sufferers, suggests Shepherd, should try not to neglect or get angry with those who are helping to care for them. Having to make all kinds of adjustments - social, emotional, domestic, financial -as a result of someone being close to a person developing C.F.S./M.E. can be a very stressful experience. (The carer may be able to claim Invalid Care Allowance if he/she cares for a sufferer for at least 35 hours per week and if they receive DLA care component at the middle or higher rates) (Shepherd, 2001).

10 Alternative and complementary approaches

If the sufferer has faith in approaches such as homoeopathy or acupuncture, then these are probably worth a try - but they should make sure they find a reputable practitioner. Unfortunately, some members of the alternative and complementary health sector make completely unjustified claims about their ability to treat and even cure C.F.S./M.E. There is no scientific evidence to support the view that magnetic devices, immune system supplements, anti-candida diets, megadosing on vitamins, or highly restrictive anti-allergy diets are of any value in the treatment of ME/C.F.S.

Shepherd, C. (2001) M.E. Association magazine Perspectives, 10 important aspects of the self-management of C.F.S./M.E.

***

C.F.S./M.E. appears to have multiple causes, producing multiple physical damage which probably will require multiple treatments. It is my conjecture that for myself, it was probably the combined effects of organo-phosphate pesticide exposure reducing the immune system, a viral infection, over-work and then two courses of antibiotics following each other that allowed the virus to penetrate deep into muscle and brain cells precipitating C.F.S./M.E.

An article entitled "M.E. My cure for this terrible mystery illness" by Emily Wilcox (Ester Rantzen's daughter who suffers from C.F.S./M.E.) in the Daily Mail (16-10-01, p56) mentions that the Government's working party into the best ways to manage C.F.S./M.E. published its report on 11 January 2002 (The Report of the C.F.S./M.E. Working Group to the Chief Medical Officer (2002). To see this report go to www.doh.gov.uk then insert " C.F.S./M.E. working group" into the search box, then scan down the list to find it.

It says that York University has carried out a review of all the treatments for the illness. They have found that the only treatments proven to show a positive effect on C.F.S./M.E. are Cognitive Behavioural Therapy (C.B.T. tackling the emotional or psychological aspect of the illness) and graded exercise (which improves energy and physical strength). Both of these helped Emily Wilcox but she gives a caution that both if not carefully implemented can worsen the condition. C.B.T. sometimes called Cognitive Behavioural Counselling, can correct the erroneous beliefs that can trap a sufferer in the illness.

Emily was diagnosed with C.F.S./M.E. in 1995 following glandular fever and although very tired and in pain, a consultant told her to pull her socks up and go back to school. She did – and collapsed two months later.

Eventually she was so exhausted that in 1998 she was in a wheelchair, hospitalised and unable to get out of bed, sit up or hold a book, living in a twilight world.

However, under a consultant neurologist, Professor Leslie Findley at The National ME Centre (for the address, see the section entitled 'SPECIALIST C.F.S./M.E. CLINICS IN THE U.K.') she was told that C.F.S./M.E. is a self-correcting illness with only 20 per cent of patients being trapped in it for good. Of the remaining 80 per cent, 60 per cent make a complete return to health and the others have active lives, on condition they paced themselves.

Under Professor Findley's care Emily says that she has so improved that she can work, use public transport and even stay out late sometimes. (To say she is 'cured' as in the title of the article may be therefore misleading).

The graded exercise treatment for Emily started with being lifted into a chair to sit for 15 minutes per day. This was increased gradually so that by the end of a **year** she was able to walk around the house unaided. Eventually she alternated exercise with half-hour rests through-out the day.

In a recent article in the Mail on Sunday, Supplement 'You' for the 29-9-02 pages 33-34 the case of another teenage girl's recovery from C.F.S./M.E. is described. Initially the girl Juliet was diagnosed with postviral syndrome and then later with M.E. by a paediatrician. She and her parents decided that Juliet should try to build up to a normal life again by doing a little more each day. This resulted in total exhaustion. Going on-line Juliet's mother found medical journal articles which described a cure for M.E. recognised by the medical profession but apparently resisted by the M.E. self-help groups because it does not involve medication. It is a programme of **physical rehabilitation.** Juliet's parents found that the Chronic Fatigue Unit (CFU) at King's College Hospital, London was the nearest centre to them offering an M.E. rehabilitation programme.

The programme involved doing everything possible to promote blood flow, by resting sitting up, regularly moving the feet and toes and avoiding excessive sleep as this can apparently be a cause of fatigue as much as lack of sleep. She slept nine hours at night and avoided dozing during the day. Next she was to increase by a very small amount the physical activity she did and decrease her rest slightly and to remain at this level until any symptoms settled. Only then was she to make the next tiny change. Once she could cope with a short walk to the end of her road, she increased this to two and three times when symptoms settled again. Within six months she was doing four half-hour walks a day. Then the education authority provided home-teaching to prepare her for a return to school. Over nine months Juliet built up to a total recovery.

In February 2002 the CFU published an evaluation of their C.F.S./M.E. rehabilitation programme for teenage sufferers. Many of these patients had been ill for 2 years or more but within a year 95 per cent are back to school full-time. Apparently the Association of Young people with M.E. (AYME) has not told their members of this programme. Juliet's parents feel sorry for the patients who know nothing of this programme from which they might benefit. They feel their daughter is cured.

The editorial comment with the article suggests that C.F.S./M.E. patients when they fall ill either push themselves too hard or commit to endless total rest; both are judged to be detrimental.

Patients generally go on to avoid all physical activity, become deconditioned with poor blood circulation, poor sleep and then anxiety about their state. Some apparently enter a 'boom or bust' cycle; saving up energy for special events then collapsing.

Juliet was lucky not to experience relapses to exhaustion caused by a slight excess of physical activity, something some C.F.S./M.E. sufferers experience when trying to implement graded exercise on their own.

Something that appears to be lacking in the research literature is a good longitudinal study of C.F.S./M.E. sufferers from soon after the illness commenced, for 15 to 20 years, reassessing them annually with a view to charting the progress of the illness. The data could be analysed using neural network software to discover the characteristics of those who recover best and those who do not.

For anyone the future can sometimes appear bleak. In the wake of individual dysfunction and illness, emanating from the damage to children of broken marriages and one parent families, more demanding less empathetic schooling and work, combined with the continuing health risks of agro-chemicals and pesticides - medical, psychological and social problems among the population are set to grow in the new millennium and so too is the prevalence of C.F.S./M.E.

Careful **self-management** is a skill everyone will benefit from – not just those with C.F.S./M.E. or chronic illness.

FURTHER READING
(Books and journal papers; Medline and psycINFO searches; see below).

A search of the free medical database website Entrez-PubMed at www.ncbi.nlm.nih.gov./PubMed - searching on 'chronic fatigue syndrome' for English language studies will provide the latest references. Then further references about the psychology of chronic fatigue syndrome can found at www.psycinfo.com a database of 1830 psychology journals.

PART 3 REFERENCES
Abrams, L. (2003). Chronic Fatigue Syndrome (Diseases and Disorders Series). Lucent Books.

Argyle, M. (1993). The Psychology of Happiness. London: Routledge.

Bell, D. S. (1995). The Doctor's Guide to Chronic Fatigue Syndrome: Understanding, Treating, and Living with CFIDS. Perseus Books.

Bell, D. S. (1999). Doctor's Guide to Chronic Fatigue Syndrome: Understanding, Treating & Living with C.F.S./M.E. Diane Pub. Co.

Benson, H. & Stark, M. (1996). Timeless Healing. The Power and Biology of Belief. Pocket Books.

Berne, K. (2001). Chronic Fatigue Syndrome, Fibromyalgia and Other Invisible Illnesses: A Comprehensive and Compassionate Guide. Hunter House Inc.

Blum, K. (1996). Disease Precepts of Reward Deficiency Syndrome. Gardner Press, U.S.A.

Brotherston, N. E. (2001). Adolescence and Myalagic Encephalomyelitis/Chronic Fatigue Syndrome: Journeys with the Dragon. Haworth Press.

Brown, P. B. (1999). Alternative Treatments for Fibromyalgia and Chronic Fatigue Syndrome: Insights from Practitioners and Patients. Publishers Group West.

Campling, F. & Sharpe, M. (2000). Chronic Fatigue Syndrome (C.F.S./M.E.): the Facts. Oxford University Press.

Chalder, T. & Deale, A. (2000). Counselling for Chronic Fatigue Syndrome. Sage Publications.

Chaudhuri, A., Behan, W.M.H. and Behan, P.O. (1998). Chronic fatigue syndrome. Proc. R. Coll. Physicians Edinb.; 28:150-163.

Chronic Fatigue Syndrome. Clinical Practice Guidelines, (2002). Working Group convened under the auspices of the Royal Australasian College of Physicians. Medical Journal of Australia, 176 S17-S55.

Cooper, S. (2000). Fibromyalgia and Chronic Fatigue:

Acutherapy and Holistic Approaches. Life Circles
Publications.

Cox, D. (2000). Occupational Therapy and Chronic Fatigue
Syndrome. Whurr Publishers.

Davies, S. M. (2000). My Daughter and ME: An account of One
Child's Struggle with ME/Chronic Fatigue Syndrome Told
from a Parent's Perspective. Association of Youth with M.E.

De Meirleir, K. (2000). Chronic Fatigue Syndrome: Critical
Reviews and Clinical Advances. Haworth Press.

Demitrack, M. A. & Abbey, S. E. (1999). C.F.S.: An Integrative
Approach to Evaluation & Treatment. Guildford Press. U.S.A.

Dossey, L. (1995). Healing Words: The Power of Prayer and the
Practice of Medicine. HarperCollins.

Duclos, M. A. (2002). If There Is Nothing Wrong With Me, Then
Why Do I Feel So Bad? The Neurologic Basis of
Fibromyalgia, Chronic Fatigue Syndrome and Related
Disorders. Writer's Showcase, Print on Demand.

Duncan, R. B. (2000). Cfids, Fibromyalgia and the Virus-allergy
link: New Therapy for Chronic Functional Illnesses. Haworth
Press.

Englebienne, P & De Meirleir, K. (2002). C.F.S.: A Biological
Approach. C.R.C. Publishers.

Fennell, (2003). Handbook of Chronic Fatigue Syndrome &
Other Fatiguing Illnesses. Chichester, Wiley.

Freeman, W.J. (1995). Societies of Brains. A study in the
neuroscience of love and hate. Hove: Lawrence Erlbaum
Associates.

Friedberg, F. & Jason, L. A. (1998). <u>Understanding Chronic</u>
<u>Fatigue Syndrome: An Empirical Guide to Assessment and</u>
<u>Treatment.</u> American Psychological Association. U.S.A.
Many mental health practitioners are recognizing C.F.S./M.E.
patients in their practice, although they are not sure how to treat
them. Written by clinical researchers this book is aimed at
mental health professions. It includes a detailed guidance
for implementing a coping-oriented C.F.S./M.E. group
program.

Gilligan, S. & Price, R. E. (1993). Therapeutic Conversations.
London: W.W. Norton.

Goldstein, A. J. (1996). <u>Betrayal by the Brain:</u> The Neurological
Basis of Chronic Fatigue Syndrome, Fibromyalgia
Syndrome and Related Neural Network Disease (the Haworth
Library of Medical Neurobiology of Somatic Disorders:
Neuroimmunoendocrine Networks in Health & Illness.
Roundhouse Publishing.

Hirshberg, C. & Barasch, M. I. (1995). <u>Remarkable Recovery</u>.
What Extraordinary Healings Can Teach Us About Getting
Well And Staying Well. Headline.

Jacobs, G. (1998). C.F.S.: <u>A Comprehensive Guide to Effective</u>
<u>Treatment.</u> Element Books HarperCollins.

Jacobs, G. (2001). <u>Chronic Fatigue Syndrome: The Natural Way.</u>
Robson Books.

Lark, S. M. (1996). C.F.S./M.E. <u>Self-help Book.</u> Celestial Arts.
USA.

Lorig, K. (1999). <u>Living a Healthy Life with Chronic Conditions</u>.
Self-Management of Heart Disease, Arthritis, Stroke,
Diabetes, Asthma, Bronchitis, Emphysema & Others. Bull

Publishers, U.S.A.

Lorig, K. & Fries, J.F. (2000). <u>Arthritis Help Book: A tested self-management program for coping with Arthritis & Fibromyalgia.</u> Perseus Books.

MacIntyre, A. (2001). <u>Chronic Fatigue Syndrome: A Practical Guide.</u> Glasgow: HarperCollins Publishers. Thorsons Health.

Martin, A. (1999). <u>Steps to Fight Chronic Fatigue Syndrome for the Modern Woman.</u> R & T Pr.

Midgley, M. (2000). <u>The Message of the Crucifixion: a spiritual guide to living with Myalgic Encephalomyelitis, Chronic Fatigue Syndrome and Fibromyalgia.</u> Book and PAL video. Overton Studios Trust.

Mulrow, C.D., Ramirez, G., Cornell, J.E., Allsup, K. (2001). Defining and managing chronic fatigue syndrome. Evidence Report/Technology Assessment No.42 (Prepared by the San Antonio Evidence-based Practice Center at the University of Texas Health Sciences Center at San Antonio. AHRQ Publication No.02-E001. Rockville (MD): Agency for Healthcare Research and quality. October (www.ahrq.gov/clinic)

(Munson, P. (2000). <u>Stricken: Voices from the Hidden Epidemic of Chronic Fatigue Syndrome.</u> Haworth Press.

Murdoch, C. & Denz-Penhey, H. (2002). <u>Chronic Fatigue Syndrome: A Patient-centered Approach</u>. (Patient-centered Care Series). Radcliffe Medical Press.

Murray, F. (1996). <u>Ginkgo Biloba</u>. Therapeutic and antioxidant properties of the 'tree of health'. New Canaan: Keats Publishing.

Murray, M. T. (1994). Getting Well Naturally: Chronic Fatigue Syndrome. Prima Publishing.

Murray, M. T. (2001). Chronic Fatigue Syndrome. Random House Publishers.

Nielson, W. R. & Weir, R. (2001). Biopsychosocial approaches to the treatment of chronic pain. Clin. J. Pain. 17 (4 Suppl.): S114-27. The U.S. Department of Health and Human Services Chronic Fatigue Syndrome Coordinating Committee State of the Science Report – "Chronic Fatigue Syndrome – State of the Science Conference/October 23-24, 2000".

Parker, J. N. (2002). The Official Patient's Sourcebook on Chronic Fatigue Syndrome. Icon Health.

Patarca-Montero, R. (2000a). Chronic Fatigue Syndrome: Critical Rreviews and Clinical Advances. Haworth Press.

Patarca-Montero, R. (2000b). Concise Encyclopedia of Chronic Fatigue Syndrome. Haworth Press.

Patarca-Montero, R. (2001). Phytotherapy of Chronic Fatigue Syndrome: Evidence-Based and Potentially Useful Botanicals in the Treatment of C.F.S. Haworth Medical Press.

Patarca-Montero, R. (2003a). Chronic Fatigue Syndrome and the Body's Immune Defense System. Haworth Press.

Patarca-Montero, R. (2003b). Chronic Fatigue Syndrome, Genes and Infection: The Eta-1/Op Paradigm. Haworth Press.

Petrie, K. & Moss-Morris, R. (2000). Chronic Fatigue Syndrome (The Experience of Illness). Routledge, an imprint of Taylor & Francis.

Richardson, J. (2001). Myalgic Encephalomyelitis/Chronic Fatigue Syndrome and Enteroviral-Mediated Organ Pathology. Haworth Medical Press.

Rossi, E. L. (1993). The Psychobiology of Mind-Body Healing. W. W. Norton.

Rotholz, J. M. (2002). Chronic Fatigue Syndrome, Christianity, and Culture: Between God and an Illness. Haworth Press.

Stoff, J. & Pellegrino, C. R. (1992). Chronic Fatigue Syndrome: The Hidden Epidemic. HarperPerennial.

Swinton, J. (2001). Spirituality and Mental Health Care. Jessica Kingsley Publishers.

Sykes, R. & Tyrrell, D. (2001). Research Methodology In Chronic Fatigue Syndrome: Proceedings of the Workshop Organised by the National Task Force on C.F.S./P.V.F.S./M.E. Westcare, U.K.

Taylor, P. J. (2002). Chronic Fatigue Syndrome: There is a Cure. Booklocker.com
Taylor, R. et al. (2001). A Clinician's Guide to Controversial Illnesses: Chronic Fatigue Syndrome, Fibromyalgia, and Multiple Chemical Sensitivities. Professional Resource Press.

Teitelbaum, J. (1999). From Fatigued to Fantastic!: A Manual for Moving Beyond Chronic Fatigue and Fibromyalgia. Avery Publishing Group.

Thompson, R. F. (1993). The Brain. A Neuroscience Primer. W. H. Freeman & Co. New York.

Trower, P., Casey, A. & Dryden, W. (1998). Cognitive Behavioural Counselling in Action. London: Sage.

Verillo, E. F. & Gellman, L. M. (1998). <u>Chronic Fatigue Syndrome.</u> Saint Martin's Press.

Voncannon, B. E. (2002). <u>Chronic Fatigue Syndrome: Living with the Unknown.</u> Writer's Club Press, Print on Demand.

Whiting, P. Bagnall, A.M. Sowden, A.J. Cornell, J.E. Mulrow, C.D. Ramirez, G. (2001). Interventions for the treatment and management of chronic fatigue syndrome. A systematic review. J.A.M.A., 286 (11): 1360-8.

Wittenberg, J. S. (1996). <u>The Rebellious Body: Reclaim Your Life from Environmental Illness or Chronic Fatigue Syndrome.</u> Perseus Books.

***

C.F.S./M.E. WEBSITES.

The search engine www.google.co.uk (or alternatively try "Ask Jeeves" at www.ask.co.uk)can be use to identify thousands of websites on the world wide web (www) about Chronic Fatigue Syndrome or the self-management of the illness based on, for example the biopsychosocial model, the link with organophosphate pesticides or use of a Christian or religious philosophy in treatment etc.

See details of Professor Malcolm Hooper's research on OPs (organo-phosphate pesticides), autism and C.F.S./M.E. at website http://osiris.sunderland.ac.uk/autism/

www.afme.org.uk is the website of Action for M.E.

www.ayme.org.uk is the website of The Association of Young People with M.E. Tel: 08451-232389.

www.doh.gov.uk is the website of the Government department, the Department of Health. Find particular reference to C.F.S./M.E. by inserting 'cfs' into the search box.

The Chronic Fatigue Syndrome Unit at King's College Hospital London (tel: 0203-228-5075) has a very useful website www.kcl.ac.uk/cfs

www.meassociation.org.uk is the website of the M.E. Association in the U.K.

www.psychnet-uk.com is the Psychology Web Directory for Mental Health Professionals, students and those wanting assistance or seeking to know more about the area of mental health. See section 'Psychological Research' for details of free libraries of books and journals on the internet.

http://ukplus.co.uk and search for 'Take M.E. Seriously', or Chronic Fatigue Syndrome or M.E.

www.WebHealth.co.uk has much information on C.F.S./M.E.

NEWSGROUPS

Newsgroups are groups of people on the internet who have a common interest or hobby. There are newsgroups for C.F.S and M.E. The M.E. Association magazine 'Perspectives' mentions alt.med.cfs as the largest ME newsgroup and uk.people.support.cfs-me is a recently formed UK ME newsgroup.

To access newsgroups the reader must contact their ISP and get the address of their newsgroup server. Then using software like 'Outlook Express' the newsgroup wizard will configure it. The reader can only access the newsgroups on their own ISP server. To access others go to www.remarq.com. The newsgroup list can be searched for M.E., me, C.F.S./M.E. alt.health.cfs is an example of a C.F.S./M.E. newsgroup.

FEEDBACK TO THE AUTHOR

I would be pleased to receive any feedback about this book from readers at the following email address:
raymondpaulgregory@blueyonder.co.uk

USEFUL RESOURCES.
Meditation tape.
Meditation Relax 2, Relaxation Centre Cassettes, from
W.H.Smiths.

White Light Meditation
From New World Music, Paradise Farm, Westhall,
Halesworth, Suffolk. IP19 8RH. Tel: 01986-891-600.
www.newworldmusic.com/uk

Relaxation tape.
From LifeSkills, Bowman House, 6, Billetfield, Taunton. TA1
3NN. Tel: 01823-451771. www.cragface.co.uk

Ultimate Relaxation.
From New World Music, Paradise Farm, Westhall,
Halesworth, Suffolk. IP19 8RH. Tel: 01986-891-600.
www.newworldmusic.com/uk

Self-confidence.
Relax For Success, Vol 1 & 2, Relaxation Centre Cassettes, from
W.H.Smiths.

Negative Thoughts.
You Can't Afford The Luxury of A Negative Thought.
Thorsons Audio, from W.H.Smiths or www.amazon.co.uk

"Quit For Life."
Smoking is very difficult to give up. Only about 3 per cent
manage it by themselves, 7 per cent with the advice of their
G.P., 16 per cent with nicotine patches but 43 per cent using the
psychological self-help programme called "Quit For Life" by
David F. Marks. No willpower is needed to successfully use this
programme. It is available from: www.amazon.co.uk

***

USEFUL ADDRESSES AND TELEPHONE NUMBERS.

Action For ME, Third Floor, Canningford House, 38 Victoria Street, Bristol. BS1 6BY
Membership: 0845 123 2380 / 0117 9279551
Telephone support: 0845 123 2314
Welfare rights helpline: 01749 330136. www.afme.org.uk

Benefit Advice Line. For people with disabilities and carers. www.direct.gov.uk

Birmingham Disability Resource Centre, Bierton Rd., South Yardley, Birmingham. B25 8PQ. Tel: 0121-789-7365. They may be able to give the address of equivalent centres around the country. www.birmingham.gov.uk

www.disability.co.uk

Carers' Helpline TEL: 0808 808 7777.
www.direct.gov.uk/en/Dl1/Directories/DG_10011166

Carers UK. (Previously Carers' National Association) 20-25 Glasshouse Yard, London. EC1A 4JT .
Carers line tel: 0808 808 7777 info@carersuk.org
http://www.carersuk.org

Carers' Unit, Birmingham Social Services Department, Birmingham Social Care and Health, Level 5, Louisa Ryland House, 44 Newhall Street, Birmingham B3 3PL
Telephone: 0121-464 3123. Other local authorities may have a similar unit.

Cruse Bereavement Care is a national charity set up to offer free, confidential help to bereaved people. Cruse produces booklets on coping with grief which you can buy on-line. Find your local branch at: www.crusebereavementcare.org.uk/

Disability Discrimination Act (1995).
www.direct.gov.uk/en/DisabledPeople/RightsAndObligations/**Dis ability**Rights/DG_4001068 -

Disability Discrimination Act (DDA) web site at
www.disability.gov.uk

M.E. Association, 4 Top Angel, Buckingham Industrial Park,
Buckingham. MK18 1TH. Tel: 01280 818968 (between 09.30
and 16.30). Website: www.meassociation.org.uk
Email: meconnect@meassociation.org.uk

M.E. Task Force. National Task Force on C.F.S./M.E. tel:0117-
923-9341. Dr. Richard Sykes, Task Force Coordinator, 155,
Whiteladies Road, Clifton, Bristol. BS8 2RF. Report on Services
for C.F.S./M.E. (Centres and Research) costs £14-95. There was a
problem updating this information at the time of publication.

Medline Update No: 52 M.E. gives medical references about M.E.
from: The Medical Information Centre, The British Library,
Boston Spa, Wetherby, West Yorkshire. LS23 7BQ.

Samaritans. Someone to talk to. Tel: 08457-90-90-90.

SPECIALIST C.F.S./M.E. CLINICS IN THE U.K.
This list is taken from the M.E. Task Force's "Report on Services for C.F.S./M.E. (Centres and Research)". See "USEFUL ADDRESSES AND TELEPHONE NUMBERS" section. However, it has been updated where possible at the time of publication but it may not be totally comprehensive. Enquires at the G.P. or local NHS Trust might find more services for C.F.S./M.E.

The National ME Centre, Disablement Services Centre, Harold Wood Hospital, Gubbins Lane, Harold Wood, Romford, Essex. RM3 OAR. Tel: 01708 378050. **Email: nmecent@aol.com** www.nmec.org.uk/contact.html

Barking, Havering and Redbridge Hospitals NHS Trust, Tel: 01708-435044. www.bhrhospitals.nhs.uk/cfs/cfshome.php

King's College Hospital, Chronic Fatigue Research & Treatment Unit, Mapother House, 1st Floor, De Crespigny Park, Denmark Hill, London SE5 8AZ. Phone: 0203 228 5075. www.kcl.ac.uk/cfs is their website where information about C.F.S./M.E. Rahabilitation programme is available.

St. James's & Seacroft University Hospitals Trust Headquarters, St James University Hospital, Beckett Street, Leeds, LS9 7TF. Tel: 0113 2065859. www.leedsteachinghospitals.com/patients/service_directory/index.php

Department of Infectious & Tropical Diseases, Coppetts Wood Hospital, Coppetts Road, Muswell Hill, London. N10 1JN. Tel: 020 7794 0500. This hospital is administered by the Royal Free Hospital. www.royalfree.org.uk/default.aspx?top_nav_id=5&tab_id=453

Institute Of Neurological Sciences, Southern General Hospital, Glasgow. G5 14TF. Tel: 0141-201-1100.
www.nhsggc.org.uk/content/default.asp?page=s762&loc_id=20

Malagay Barn, Church Road, West Tilbury, Tilbury, Essex. RM18 8TU.

Department Of Psychological Medicine, City & Hackney NHS Community Services Trust, St. Bartholomew's Hospital, London. EC1A 7BE. Tel: 020 7377 7000.

Dept Of Medicine & Infectious Diseases, University Hospital Of Wales, Heath Park, Cardiff. CF4 4XW. Tel: 029 2074 7747.

***

www.dh.gov.uk/en/Publicationsandstatistics/Pressreleases/DH 4070520
New centres and local support teams for C.F.S./M.E. patients announced. Date published: 20 January 2004.

Funded by the £8.5 million cash injection announced last year, the 12 centres will be based in Newcastle, Leeds, Liverpool, Manchester, Sheffield, Birmingham/West Midlands, East Midlands, East Anglia, North London (St Bartholomew's), Surrey (Sutton), Bath/Bristol and Cornwall/Devon. The Centres and Local Teams will champion and support the development of local services to improve the care and treatment of the many people with C.F.S./M.E.

28 local support teams spread throughout the country, will provide support to those adjusting to and coping with C.F.S./M.E.

Contact: Press Officer
Address: Media Centre, Department of Health, Richmond House, 79 Whitehall, London. SW1 2NL.**Phone: Rachel Hayward** 020 7210 5315.

There are **13 Clinical Network Coordinating Centres (CNCCs)** across England which are championing the development of services and improved clinical care for C.F.S./M.E. in their area. Each CNCC has an individual, named clinical champion or network coordinator:

- **Dr Hugh Rickards**
  Consultant Neuropsychiatrist
  Department of Neuropsychiatry
  Queen Elizabeth Psychiatric Hospital
  Mindelsohn Way
  Edgbaston
  Birmingham
  B15 2QZ
  tel: 0121 678 2019

- **Dr Hazel O'Dowd**
  Clinical Psychologist
  Pain Management Centre
  Ward 22
  Frenchay Hospital
  Frenchay Park Road
  Bristol
  BS16 1LE
  tel: 0117 975 3890

- **Professor Chris D Ward**
  Professor of Rehabilitation Medicine
  University Rehabilitation Research Unit
  Derby City General Hospital
  Uttoxeter Road
  Derby
  DE22 3NE
  tel: 01322 340131 ext 5680

- **Ms Sue Pemberton**
  Consultant Occupational Therapist

Leeds C.F.S./M.E. Service
J Ward
Seacroft Hospital
Leeds
LS14 6UH
tel: 0113 2062141

- **Dr Fred Nye**
  Consultant Physician
  Royal Liverpool University Hospital
  Infectious Diseases
  32 Link Corridor
  Prescot Street
  Liverpool
  L7 8XP
  tel: 0151 7063868

- **Dr Damien Longson**
  Consultant Liaison Psychiatrist
  North Manchester General Hospital
  Safire Unit
  Park House
  Delauneys Road
  Crumpsall
  Manchester
  M8 6AR
  0161 720 4867

- **Dr Peter D White**
  Reader in Psychological Medicine
  C.F.S./M.E. Service
  St Bartholomew's Hopsital
  PO BOX 8108
  William Harvey House
  61 Bartholomew Close
  EC1A 7BE
  tel: 0207 601 8108

JOINT WITH:

- **Dr Maurice Murphy**
  Consultant in Immunology and HIV Medicine
  C.F.S./M.E. Service
  St Bartholomew's Hopsital
  PO BOX 8108
  William Harvey House
  61 Bartholomew Close
  EC1A 7BE
  tel: 0207 601 8108

- **Dr Gavin Spickett**
  Consultant Clinical Immunologist
  Head of Regional Immunology Services
  The Newcastle upon Tyne Hospital NHS Trust
  Royal Victoria Infirmary
  Queen Victoria Road
  Newcastle upon Tyne
  NE1 4LP
  tel: 0191 2825517

- **Dr Terry Mitchell**
  Consultant Haematologist
  C/o Mrs Linda Woods, C.F.S./M.E. Service
  James Paget Healthcare NHS Trust
  Lowerstof Road
  Gorleston
  Great Yarmouth
  Norfolk
  NR13 6LA
  Tel: 01493 453321

- **Dr Selwyn Richards**
  Consultant Rheumatologist
  Poole Hospital NHS Trust

Longfleet Road
Poole
Dorset
BH15 2JB
tel: 01202 448613

- **Dr Gwyneth de Lacey**
  Head of Health and Medical Psychology
  22 Collegiate Crescent
  Sheffield
  S10 2BA
  tel: 0114 2261903

- **Dr Amolak Bansal**
  Department of Immunology
  St Helier Hospital
  Wrythe Lane
  Carshalton
  Surrey
  SM5 1AA
  tel: 020 8296 2725

- **Professor Anthony Pinching**
  Associate Dean for Cornwall
  Peninsula Medical School
  Peninsula Medical School Offices
  Royal Cornwall Hospital
  Truro
  TR1 3LJ
  Tel: 01872 252865/ 253064

If your GP does not have information about a local service, they can contact the nearest clinical champions for details. This above list was provided by www.afme.org.uk